A Candlelight Ecstasy Romance®

"DID YOU THINK YOU WERE JUST GOING TO WALK RIGHT BACK INTO MY ARMS WHEN YOU'D REJECTED ME?" CASEY ASKED COLDLY.

"I thought you understood why I left and would love me while I was gone. That's what I thought," Brian answered angrily.

"That's not the way it works, not when a man doesn't love you enough to let you be with him."

"When a man loves a woman he protects her. That's what I was trying to do for you," he snapped. "You can't begin to imagine the things that went on in that courtroom and behind the scenes. And I'll always be glad I didn't take you with me."

"I didn't ask you to protect me, and since you made that decision for me you must accept the responsibility for breaking us up. Not me. You."

CANDLELIGHT ECSTASY ROMANCES®

PERFECT ILLUSIONS

Paula Hamilton

A CANDLELIGHT ECSTASY ROMANCE®

Published by
Dell Publishing Co., Inc.
1 Dag Hammarskjold Plaza
New York, New York 10017

Dell ® TM 681510, Dell Publishing Co., Inc.

Candlelight Ecstasy Romance®, 1,203,540, is a registered
trademark of Dell Publishing Co., Inc., New York, New York.

ISBN: 0-440-16907-0

Printed in the United States of America

First printing—September 1985

Dedicated to all the women who have ever found themselves searching for the perfect illusion

To Our Readers:

We have been delighted with your enthusiastic response to Candlelight Ecstasy Romances®, and we thank you for the interest you have shown in this exciting series.

In the upcoming months, we will continue to present the distinctive sensuous love stories you have come to expect only from Ecstasy. We look forward to bringing you many more books from your favorite authors and also the very finest work from new authors of contemporary romantic fiction.

As always, we are striving to present the unique, absorbing love stories that you enjoy most—books that are more than ordinary romance. Your suggestions and comments are always welcome. Please write to us at the address below.

Sincerely,

The Editors
Candlelight Romances
1 Dag Hammarskjold Plaza
New York, New York 10017

CHAPTER ONE

"Aeyi yi yi yi yi," Casey Clayton muttered to herself. "Be still my heart."

When all the time it should have been beating time to an undemonstrative slow waltz, Casey's heart hammered out a hard rock tune: *He'd come back.* Now Brian Powell *was* back.

Brian . . . His name filled her mind, taking her back to a time when he had declared his undying love, to a time when a single longing look from him had made her breath catch in her throat and her knees grow weak.

Oh, God, help me, she cried in silent appeal. *I thought I was prepared but I'm not.*

She'd practiced all of this—how cool she'd be, how nonchalant she'd act—and even fooled herself into thinking she'd pull it off. At the ripe old age of twenty-eight Casey was sitting in a cubicle in a dingy, cramped newspaper office locked in a fierce internal struggle with herself, trying with panicked desperation to stop her cheeks from coloring crimson, but she was losing. Her heart was ricocheting around inside her chest and her knees had turned to dishwater.

Brian Powell walked toward her desk, a happy

smile radiating across his face, lighting up his pale-gray eyes and widening his full mouth to show a row of perfect white teeth. Some things never changed, she thought. The man was still a dentist's dream.

Casey swallowed hard and plastered on a slick smile. She was trapped, caught behind her desk with no place to run, no place to hide.

As swift as lightning flashes across the skies, Casey felt a swell of pain. She tried unsuccessfully to hide it. She couldn't let him see how much she hurt.

"Hello, Casey. How've you been?"

Now was the time for her to make some clever comment; some witticism certainly seemed in order, but nothing was funny. "I've been just fine."

Casey wiped her hand on her skirt to make certain there was no telltale moisture and then brought it up and stretched it out across her desk, awaiting a formal handshake. Instead Brian Powell took her hand and placed it across his palm, then held it there.

"It's been quite a while. Let's see . . . almost a year. Right?"

His voice was low and full of a raspy intensity that she'd always found compelling, like a radio disc jockey's. With that voice of his he had the power to make people want to listen to whatever he had to say. It was a subtle talent, but, nevertheless, a profound one, one he had used to his advantage when he had been a staff reporter.

She raised her eyes to meet his. Precisely thirteen months, four days, and six and a half minutes, she wanted to tell him.

"Sounds like something Humphrey Bogart might say to a leading lady," Casey joked, still holding tight

12

to the fake smile she'd chosen earlier. It seemed very important that she play the role of a vaudeville comic right now. She couldn't allow the pain to show through.

Since she had heard that he'd bought the newspaper, she'd been rehearsing what she'd say when they met again. In front of the mirror, when driving to work, while taking her daily three-mile walk—anywhere, everywhere, whenever he came to mind—and that seemed far, far too often—she'd practice her speech. Her smile turned sincere for a second. A lot of good her practicing had done. For the life of her she couldn't remember the words she'd planned to say. They'd flown out the same window as her sophistication.

Laughing softly, Brian smiled down at her, feeling her hand grow warm inside his own. Now that he finally had hold of her he wasn't about to let go. "You haven't changed one bit, Casey. Still as funny as ever."

In one seemingly relaxed maneuver he eased himself onto the edge of her desk, twisted his head to the side, and studied her for a moment, his eyes full of curiosity. "I take that back. There's something different but I'm not sure exactly what it is." He shrugged, unable to put his finger on it. "Anyway, I'm glad to see you again."

Something different? Casey stifled a laugh. Only thirty-two pounds of something, Mr. Powell, she wanted to shout. Look at me! I have bones—cheekbones, rib bones, and hip bones now. I have shrunk and returned as a smaller version of myself. I've lost almost one fifth of a body. She wished she'd worn her new green dress, the one that fit snug across her hips,

13

instead of the blouson lavender dress she had on. Then maybe he would have noticed.

Trying not to seem obtuse, Brian nevertheless continued to look down at her. She was the same, yet different. With golden-blond hair, large blue-green almond-shaped eyes, and cheekbones like cut crystal, Casey was as beautiful as his mind had recalled since the last time he'd seen her. The cheekbones seemed a little more pronounced, perhaps, but she was the same person.

He hadn't forgotten the soft, playful mouth that gave the hint of a wry smile at the corners and turned absolutely delightful when it opened to burst into one of those quick bolts of laughter and ended up with the gurgling Goldie Hawn giggle Casey was so well known for. But thinking about the woman from a far-off distance was nothing like being with her. It was as different as seeing an ad in a magazine for a ski trip and actually going. There was no comparison.

Casey stifled a grimace. In her mind she could see the thousands and thousands of pores inside her hand begin to open and perspiration bead out. In a move she hoped looked casual, she took her hand away. "And now that you're back and my new boss, I don't know how to address you: Brian or Mr. Powell?"

"Is that a joke?"

"I don't know. Are you laughing?"

Oh, no, you don't, she thought. *I'm a little dingy but I'm not double-digit dingy.* He was being too friendly, too intimate already, and she wanted nothing to do with any part of it. As much as her heart thrilled at seeing him, she wouldn't let herself forget how much she'd already suffered.

14

The minute she'd heard the news that Brian Powell was returning to Austin as the new publisher of the *Texas Daily* she'd vowed to be "off-limits" to him. In the interest of self-preservation she had to make good on that vow now.

Thirteen months ago Brian had left the newspaper and the state. If that wasn't enough, he'd also left behind a woman who'd tumbled head over heels into an emotional tailspin and landed with a big splat and a broken heart. He'd left her. He'd said he was doing it to protect her, because he loved her so much.

Never mind that she had fallen for him like a ton of bricks. Never mind that she had thought he loved her in the same way. He'd gone back to Pennsylvania to finalize his divorce, and he wanted to keep her out of it, he'd explained. His about-to-be-ex-wife Sheila was threatening to name Casey as corespondent, even though Brian and Sheila had been legally separated for almost a year.

Brian said he couldn't let Casey suffer the indignities of being dragged through the legal garbage that would be slung. He'd go back and take the time to settle things with Sheila for once and all. Sheila only wanted a piece of his family money, anyway.

Yet Casey had wanted nothing more than to be with the man she loved. She wanted to stand by him through whatever tragedies befell them. She loved him. Couldn't he understand that? Unwilling to see things her way, he'd packed his bags and left Texas, taking her broken heart along.

She'd never forget the agony on his face, the pain in his eyes. If she'd still had a heart left at that point, he'd have wrenched it away from her with his woeful

15

look of despair. But it was too late. He'd already broken her heart and she stood in mute silence watching him leave, sick to death at the loss. It was a matter of differing beliefs, but they were differences too great to be resolved.

Brian spoke up. "Casey, did you hear me?" He peered down at her, frowning.

Busy with her memories, she hadn't heard him, so she just kept smiling up at him, waiting. Surely he'd have the grace to repeat himself, she thought, but he didn't.

"Anyway, why don't you let me take you to dinner and we'll talk about everything."

"Sorry. I've already made dinner plans. And if I hadn't, I'd still be busy. I'm cleaning out my refrigerator. Things inside it are beginning to move."

Undaunted, Brian ignored her banter. "I wanted to take you someplace down on Sixth Street. Since I've been gone I hear there are a lot of new restaurants open."

"Have you ever seen a refrigerator levitate across the room?"

"So, how about tomorrow night? What do you say?"

"I say thanks but no thanks. I'm busy, really."

She raised her eyes quickly to his, trying to end anything before it could emerge. Staring at him, she waited to hear what he'd say next, hoping he'd have the grace to leave.

He'd let his black hair grow longer on the top so that it fell slightly off-center of his forehead. The sides were clipped close to his head, a cross between the preppy look and the sportsman. She liked it but she wouldn't dare tell him so.

"What is it?" he asked with a trace of crossness in his voice. "Are you going with someone? I don't see an engagement ring."

"Why should that make a difference?" she asked him, suddenly angry that he'd come back, angrier still that he was trying to start things up again. "I'm not interested in going anywhere with you. Not now. It's too late," she lashed out.

"Well, I'm back and this time I'm not leaving," he said in all seriousness.

"Hail, hail. Should we send up cheers?"

"No."

"Then what is it you want from me?"

Brian felt her hostility wash over him, leaving him with a suffocating feeling, as if he were trying to breathe underwater. "Casey, out of all the people I know in this town, your opinion means the most to me. I'd like to talk to you about the newspaper, get your view on conditions, and find out what you think about my buying the paper."

She watched him, her eyes trying to penetrate into his thoughts. After a few seconds she said, "I'll save you the price of a meal. I think it's going to be a definite improvement."

"Why?"

"Because you don't have sideburns like the former publisher, Mr. Bartok, and you don't go around pinching all the women's behinds." She paused. "Do you? I mean now that I think about it, maybe that behavior goes with the territory."

Casey really was glad Bartok was gone. His ideas

17

had grown as stale as his jokes. Alfred Bartok looked more like an old traveling salesman than a newspaperman. His face had more lines than a Connecticut road map and the top of his head was shiny bald. To compensate he had grown enormous sideburns.

Brian watched her. As uncomfortable as she had made him feel, he found himself smiling. No matter what else happened, Casey always had that powerful sense of humor of hers. She was like a fresh breath of sunshine.

"I missed you."

The caress of his voice was almost too much. She had worked so hard to forget him and now there he was, warm seductive memories returning in the flesh.

"I mean it. I really missed you."

Brian moved his lanky body nearer to the middle of her desk so that he was directly above her, his leg practically touching her knee. His pale-gray eyes studied her face; the corners of his mouth crinkled into a gentle smile.

"You have no idea."

Her lips were slightly parted, soft, inviting. Her eyes were bright and alert. He knew what her lips would feel like if he were to touch them with his own. He'd thought of it every day and night since he'd been away. It had kept him going when times were the roughest, and he'd prayed she'd still be there when he returned.

At that moment he was so close to her that she could smell the lemony tang of his after-shave and feel the warmth his nearness brought with him. *Whatever in the world possessed you to make you think he could be forgotten?* she complained to herself.

18

Long ago she'd told herself she was over him, but then she hadn't dreamed he'd ever come back. Now all her visions of being able to handle the situation were failing miserably. She felt as if her blood pressure were shooting sky high.

She wished the floor would open up and swallow her, give her a minute to think of some clever witticism, powder her nose, and then pop her back up. Unfortunately, she didn't move and the only thing she could think of to do was roll her eyes in exasperation.

"Casey," he said, bending toward her.

"Don't start this, Brian." She raised her hand in protest and pushed her chair back. "Just don't—"

"I'm trying to tell you something."

"Something I don't want to hear," she protested. "Did you honestly think you could just walk back into my life and pick up where we left off?" She was fighting against the tears that stung her eyes and at the same time was searching for the strength she'd thought she'd developed within herself.

Once more those eyes held hers. An electric silence fell between them.

She couldn't help but remember how their relationship had begun innocently, as so many do, working together. Casey, fascinated by this handsome man with the driving personality; Brian, needing someone to befriend him as he went through what he described as a sticky divorce from a miserable marriage. Without their choosing, so it seemed to Casey, their relationship had blossomed and taken on a life of its very own, short but magical.

Brian kept watching her, carefully trying to assess her feelings. He saw nothing warm in her eyes. Those

19

almond-shaped eyes of hers had always turned a shade darker when she was angry. In the early days of their relationship they had been a softer green. Toward the end it seemed they were dark too often.

With a shrug of his shoulders, he resigned himself. "Okay, I'll give up . . . for a while." He got up from the desk and started out of her office cubicle.

As she watched him go, she tried to get herself under control. The last half hour had been an ordeal and she felt ravaged by it. And because it was her birthday, it all seemed especially untimely.

"I know what it is." Brian turned abruptly and pointed an accusing finger directly at her. "You've done something to your hair. A new style. That's it." With a crisp snap of his fingers he walked away.

Self-consciously she brought one hand up to brush a strand of hair behind her ear. It was true. She had let her hair grow all one length after seeing a picture of a swank, starving model in *Vogue* magazine. People had told her that having her hair cut so that it curled under right at her nape had added a touch of chic to her slender new image.

But she didn't believe them. In her mind she was still a plump woman who looked attractive and neat but nothing more. When friends insisted she was sexy-looking with her angular face and huge almond-shaped eyes, she couldn't relate their opinions to her self-image.

Now she bent down over her work, trying to banish the swell of emotions Brian's return had caused. Silently she read an ad she was to place in the newspaper.

HEALTHY, WEALTHY, WISE—but not smart enough to have met that special woman. I'm slim, athletic, 6', 40's, male, intellectually inclined, a combination of independent and dependent. Professional interests in art, music, media, natural history. A Renaissance man. I want special friendship with multifaceted, sensual, real beauty inside and out. Reply to Box 40, city.

"Well, don't we all, Garfield," she said aloud as she corrected a few minor spelling errors. She looked at the stationery, observing the solid feel of the paper and the watermark on the sheet. From the looks of his letter he might be telling the truth. He'd chosen good paper, at least.

The next one was the last.

SILLINESS NEEDED—Successful, attractive woman executive, 39, too involved in work and grad school to giggle enough. Are you a man successful and secure enough to play? I like business, psychology, reading, travel, pinball. I'm warm, feminist, politically liberal; you probably are too.

Immediately Casey scratched that part. How on earth would the person know?

What would be a sensational first date with a stranger? And please tell me enough so we aren't strangers. Include your phone number. Box 8821-B, City.

That's enough work for one day, she decided, and began to clean off her desk. She heard footsteps outside her office cubicle and she couldn't help but think that it might be Brian. When the footsteps passed, she was filled with a sense of disappointment. She'd thought maybe he'd try to talk to her again. But that way of thinking was a big mistake, she cautioned herself, and tried to push him out of her mind.

She began to think of food. After all she'd been through that day there was a strong possibility that she could eat a horse. Being around Brian had made her nervous; food would be a soothing balm. But she stopped herself in midstream. *Think of how good you look now, Casey, and what a struggle it's been to get there.*

When she and Brian had broken up she'd tried bit by bit, piece by piece, to start her life over again. She had convinced herself that her love for him had only been an illusion, albeit what she had temporarily termed a perfect illusion. And after a while, as she had accustomed herself to the grief, she had rationalized her way into a decision. She could remain hopelessly wretched and miserable or she could change her life . . . change everything about herself. Finally she had made up her mind. She'd change—she'd become a different Casey, one who wouldn't feel any sort of attraction to a man like Brian.

Thinking about what she'd accomplished, Casey sucked in her cheeks, feeling their hollowness, then put away some file folders and took out her handbag. At least she had the night to look forward to. Her six special friends, all members of an organization she'd started when she'd found others who wanted to lose weight, were taking her out to Vegetarian Village for a birthday celebration. They called themselves SWITCH, Six Women In To Changing Habits, and she loved each and every one of them.

Fighting down the intrusive vision of a rich, gooey, fudge sundae, she tried to concentrate on what she'd wear to celebrate her birthday. But every time she rid herself of the sundae idea, Brian's face popped up in its place. Brian was back, she told herself, but she had no intention of putting her emotions on the line again. She'd learned her lesson.

23

CHAPTER TWO

Casey hurriedly left the newspaper office by the side door. As she dashed to her car, the heat hit her with the force of a heavy blow. She kept her head down as she ran, thinking of how she'd promised her mother she'd stop by on her way home, wondering if she should tell her that Brian had returned to Austin.

She had no interest in talking about him right now, let alone in thinking about him. She drove out of the parking lot and headed across town. One thing she was sure of: The more she was around him, the greater the chance of reliving old heartaches. The dreamer in her wished it weren't so. The realist said it was written in stone.

Casey drove up in front of The Green Chile Ice House, parked next to her mother's bright-red Cadillac convertible, and got out. From inside she could hear a wailing country tune blaring from the jukebox and the accompanying sound of heated voices.

The Green Chile Ice House was owned and managed by her mother. Mildred Clayton had bought it six weeks after Casey's father had died, and it was the subject of much ill will between Mildred's children. Casey hadn't been particularly surprised when her

24

mother had bought it, recognizing her mother's decided bent toward individuality and wanting her to find a new life to stave off the loneliness widowhood could bring.

But Casey's oldest sister, Callie, had had a screeching fit, claiming their father would turn over in his grave, after he'd left every member of the family enough money so they could live the rest of their lives in comfort. But Mildred Clayton wasn't a woman looking for comfort. She was more interested in people. She'd always been a people person, and The Green Chile Ice House was certainly a place to meet people, all kinds.

When anyone else tried to ask for an explanation Mildred had only replied, "An idle widow is a troubled widow." It hadn't taken long for her reputation to spread, and soon she had a loyal clientele who knew where to go for the strongest shots of good whiskey, ice-cold beer, even free bar snacks from four to six daily. And if Mildred gave them a stream of conversation peppered with her own personal brand of advice and philosophy, no one seemed to mind. At any rate no one had ever had the nerve to say he did.

Casey stepped inside the partially darkened half convenience store, half bar. "Hello," she called.

"Okay," Mildred called out, "hit it." Immediately she burst into song followed by a half-dozen warped voices. "Happy birthday to you, happy birthday to you . . ."

Having guessed her mother would do something like this, Casey stood in the center of the store, a gentle smile on her face. She wasn't about to tell them that their voices sounded more like the screeches of fighting cats than any melodic birds. When they finished Casey bowed. "Thank you, thank you," she called over the noise from the jukebox.

Her mother came out from behind the bar. "Here she is, folks, the sweetest baby girl I have."

Casey hugged her mother, trying in vain to keep from being suffocated by all the hair. About the only thing consistent about Mildred Clayton was the way she wore her hair. Back in the sixties she'd gone to the Chat 'n Curl Beauty Shop and come home with a hairstyle that had always reminded Casey of the gold helmets the San Francisco Forty Niners wore. Mildred had loved it and faithfully went to the Chat 'n Curl Beauty Shop every Thursday morning at nine o'clock to have her helmet fixed, curled, and lacquered down so that not even a full-gale hurricane could move a single hair on her head.

"Hi, Mom," Casey said with a smile.

"Cake! We've got a cake." Mildred grabbed Casey's arm and pulled her over to a chrome-legged red-and-white Formica table where Aunt Wetonnah sat waiting.

"It's beautiful," Casey told her, then bent down to hug Wetonnah Winslow, Mildred's sister.

Casey had dreaded this all day long, thinking her mother and her aunt would get into their favorite birthday discussion, the one they had every year: the fate of their unmarried daughters. Casey had come to believe that the two sisters looked upon each single daughter's birthday as something akin to a wake. The only thing missing was the coffin.

"Well," her mother said with a pleased giggle, "let's light the candles." The cake was decorated with blue

26

icing and blue candles, and on top there was the shape of a woman outlined in brown and red, reading a book.

All of the customers in The Green Chile Ice House gathered round, two or three of them looking like they might be "in their cups," so to speak. Wetonnah sat daintily lighting the candles, taking her time, and Casey found herself wondering if they'd burn down before she managed to get them all lit.

"Now, blow them out and make a wish." Her mother beamed. "And I bet I know what you'll wish for." She raised her eyebrows and winked knowingly at her sister.

When Casey had blown them all out, her aunt said with pride, "I know this year will be it. This is the year when Casey will find the man of her dreams. I can feel it in my bones."

Wetonnah's bones had been giving her messages for as long as anyone in the family could remember. The times her bones predictions didn't come true, she dismissed it as false readings from her arthritis, but whenever she was proven correct she ecstatically claimed it was all in the bones.

Casey looked over at her aunt and good-naturedly patted her hand. "Maybe I'll just have a good life, Aunt Wetonnah. I'm not worried about finding a man. Only you and Momma are."

Wetonnah sat there, her blue-gray hair springing up from her head like a starched flag, her angelically small round face happily looking around to see who wanted some of the birthday cake. "Maybe you're right, Casey, but out of three girls in your family

27

there's only one married and then there's my little Sandy. God forbid, she may never marry."

"Oh, Wetonnah, let up," Mildred interrupted, snatching the knife from her sister's hand and slicing the cake in erratic little squares. "When the time is right she'll find the man."

"But, Mildred, I pray to God it's before she's too old to . . ." Wetonnah rolled her eyes and looked around at the people taking the offered birthday cake.

"You all run on now," Mildred said in a loud voice, shooing her customers away from the table. "This is family." She stalked back to the bar and brought out six brown bottles of Lone Star. "Eat your cake and sip your suds. I'll be with you in a minute."

"As I was saying," Wetonnah went on in her soft, whispery little voice. "I pray Casey gets married before she's too old to have children. I asked our family doctor about it once." She waved her hands at Casey and Mildred. "Not about Casey, specifically, but about all our girls," she explained hastily. "Anyway, he said they're such strong, healthy women they still had many years left."

"See, see, Wetonnah, you worry too much."

Casey sat there with a bemused smile on her face. The conversation was going exactly as she could have predicted.

"Mildred"—Wetonnah raised her voice—"what does he know? He's never been pregnant."

"So happy birthday to me," Casey interrupted, wanting to get on with it all. "I've got time for one bite of cake. Shall we?" She took a piece and put it on a napkin.

"For good luck you've got to eat it all, Casey."

Mildred scowled at Wetonnah. "No, she doesn't. She's lost some weight and she's working hard to keep it off. I've promised no more stories about the dying children in Asia and no more urging her to eat up. Don't you start, Wetonnah."

"Okay, okay."

Casey smiled. Her weight loss had taken grit and a determination she hadn't even known she had, and she knew her mother and her aunt were proud of her.

Wetonnah weighed ninety-nine pounds on a good day and her sister Mildred weighed only twenty pounds more. They'd never had a weight problem. They believed that hearty eating was the key to good living, having been raised to cook three huge meals a day, and they'd urged their children to follow suit. It was their belief that food could cure everything from a headache to a broken heart, and they'd tried to pass their philosophy on to the next generation.

If anyone had ever had the gall to accuse either one of the former Thomas sisters of being slightly domineering or bossy, the women would have been highly offended. The truth of the matter was that saying they would be highly offended was putting it mildly, Casey decided with a private little smile. They were two loving sisters, loyal to their past and their families, eccentrics to the core.

"You know, Casey, I've been thinking." Her mother spoke up. "What about Brian Powell?" She licked a spot of icing off her finger. "Has he taken over the paper yet?"

Casey smiled and gave her head a little shake. Sometimes her mother was absolutely psychic. "Today —as a matter of fact."

"Are you going to see him again?" Mildred asked through a final mouthful of cake.

"No."

"Why not. Has he remarried or something?"

Surprising, Casey thought. She hadn't thought to ask him— Then she stopped her thoughts in midstream. Why should she have bothered asking? She wasn't interested in his personal life.

In her mind she'd spent the past year designing an image of Brian—excessively rich, too attractive, strong personality, sports minded, athletic—the antithesis of what she now wanted. She kept ticking off all the things she would like to resist about him, telling herself that she wanted just a common, average, everyday sort of guy, a man of moderation, one who'd be easy on the nerves.

Casey liked having everything solid and secure. That was why she'd even kept all her fat clothes. If anything happened she'd always have them ready.

"Now then, isn't that something, his being back in Austin and all? I told you, it's in the bones." Wetonnah began brushing crumbs off the table. "Now let's give her the presents."

Casey didn't want to talk about Brian. There was nothing she could say that could explain how much his return had upset her. She looked down at her watch, trying not to appear too eager to leave. "Mother, what have you two cooked up? Let's see," Casey said, suddenly curious to see what their gifts could be.

Casey opened up her mother's gift first. Inside were three separate items: a large wok, a beautifully bound book with blank pages, and a gold-plated fountain pen.

Mildred was grinning from ear to ear awaiting Casey's verdict, her dark-green eyes alight with pleasure. Wetonnah busied herself straightening the crooked-looking bow on her gift.

"For your gourmet cooking and your novel writing," Mildred said, alluding to Casey's newly developed skills as a gourmet cook and her unfulfilled ambition to be a novelist.

"Now mine," Wetonnah demanded impatiently as Casey thanked her mother.

While Casey opened her aunt's gift, her mother disposed of the wrapping paper. Casey opened the next box and found a jade-colored bra and matching panties of the most delicate lace and shiny satin she'd ever seen. The pieces were exquisite.

"Aunt Wetonnah, thank you." Casey smiled. "They're beautiful."

"You're welcome, darling." Wetonnah blushed happily.

"You want to know what she said when she bought them?" Mildred demanded. Then, not giving Casey a chance to say yes or no, she continued, "Wetonnah thought you might need these dainty little things for a special event." Mildred wrinkled up her face and gave Casey an elaborate wink.

"You children don't listen to me, but I still say you should buy your undergarments as though someone else might see them," Wetonnah explained.

Casey's full-blown laughter stirred them to life and soon the three were laughing uproariously, ignoring the curious stares of The Green Chile Ice House customers.

She gave each of them a kiss on the cheek and prepared to go. Though both of them tried to convince Casey to stay a little while longer she resisted, mentioning the lateness of the hour and her friends' dinner plans.

After Casey drove into the driveway of her brick home and stepped out of the car, she snapped on the ground lights behind the garage, banishing away the darkness. She opened the wrought-iron gate and went across the mist-shrouded yard along the brick walk to the kitchen door. Temptation, her white Persian cat, sat on the back wall, washing her face. Earlier in the morning before work, Casey had tried to coax her with milk and liver but Temptation remained stubbornly aloof, unwilling to acknowledge anyone's existence other than her own, even the one who fed and cared for her.

"I ought to take you to the animal pound. Then you'd find out how tough life could be, Temptation."

Casey stopped at the French door leading into her galley kitchen and looked around. She was proud of her home. It was the most tranquil of places. Set in one of Austin's old residential sections of town, the small Tudor house had a high-pitched roof, big comfortable rooms, and the most inviting backyard she'd ever seen. The moment she'd seen it she'd fallen in love with the dozens of rose bushes and free-growing flowers, which the former owners had planted. By the time she'd walked through the house and found a room she could convert into a study for her writing, she was committed. She had signed the papers that same day.

The day she'd moved in she'd found Temptation in the back garden and accepted the fact that she'd laid claim to the house first, hoping for a peaceful coexistence. Temptation wasn't at all sure she wanted the new owner, until she'd found that Casey encouraged birds with filled birdbaths and feeders abounding in the yard, and as a result they were still together after six years.

"Hello there."

He came out of the shadows with a light step and Casey heard him at the precise time she saw him. Fear froze her to the spot.

"Brian, what are you doing here?"

"Hoping you'd come home and invite me in before the rain started." He held his hand upward as if expecting rain to begin pouring into his open palm at any moment.

She looked up into an empty sky, then pushed open the door and flicked on the wall switch, bathing the homey kitchen with its antique chopping block and row after row of hanging copper pots in soft, glowing light.

She laid her purse and keys down purposefully, then turned back so she stood blocking his entrance. "I don't want to seem rude but I'm pushed for time. What precisely do you want?"

"I want to take you to dinner."

He was thinking of how lonely he had been without her in the past year. He was thinking of how awful it would be if he couldn't get her back. Even after all the misery she'd caused him, he loved her.

33

Thirteen months ago, just as he and Casey were discovering how much they cared for one another, he'd been forced to return to Pennsylvania. Casey had wanted to go with him while he went to court to finalize his long drawn-out divorce. But he couldn't take her, not since it meant she'd be forced to become a part of the nasty trial that he knew was coming. She'd turned on him then, accusing him of not loving her enough, of not wanting her to be a part of his life.

"I already told you I was busy."

"Tomorrow night then," he insisted.

"Sorry."

"Then the next night or the night after that."

"No. I'm telling you no," she declared grimly. "No date."

"Casey, why do you think I've come back here?"

"For the newspaper, I guess. But I don't care, Brian. I just want you to leave me alone."

"Okay, however you want it."

"Want it?" She gave a wry laugh. "Want what?"

"However you want things to be with us I'll agree to. I'm willing to go along with anything." His eyes watched how she reacted as she thought over what he said. "Whatever you want. However you want."

"Oh, Brian. Why did you have to . . ." She'd started to say "come back" but she stopped. Even as she spoke she felt as though she were betraying herself.

He read her thoughts. "Foolish question."

She kept her eyes downward, refusing to look at him. Her shoulders drooped with the heavy weight of disappointment.

"I know a way you can get rid of me."

"How?" she asked, her heart beating loudly in her ears. He was making her more uncomfortable by the minute. She felt she'd do anything to get rid of him. Seeing him was too powerful a reminder of their yesterdays.

He grinned playfully down at her. "Invite me in for one quick drink."

She tried to stay firm and solemn but with his wheedling came a tantalizing grin and a challenge in his eyes. The combination was every bit as devastating as she remembered.

"One drink," he repeated.

She frowned, looked down at her watch and back up at him. Finally she sighed, deciding one drink wouldn't hurt, and she moved inside. "Okay, a quick one."

Brian followed her lead before stepping around her through the kitchen and into the living area. The house was casual and inviting, nothing at all like the formal ones he'd been in all his life. It smelled of a lavish combination of vanilla and cinnamon and made him think that he could come in, take off his shoes, and completely relax. He'd missed it.

Dark beams ran from the kitchen, along the length of a long rectangular room, and ended on one side at a flagstone fireplace. One wall was of paned glass, opening up to a view of the lush green gardens beyond the brick patio outside.

"The inside of the house looks like it's been repainted since I was here last," he commented, still looking around, taking everything in from the stacks of current hardbacks on the coffee table to the overflowing pot of yellow daisies on the wooden kitchen table.

"Lots of changes take place in a year, Brian. What would you like to drink?" Casey walked over to a bar that was tucked inside an alcove on one section of the far kitchen wall. Quickly she took out two glasses and waited for his answer, her readiness to be rid of him all too apparent.

"Scotch on the rocks, if you have it."

She poured his drink and a Perrier for herself. "Here you are," she said, following him into the living area and looking out at the view he seemed so taken with.

"Thanks."

She waited for him to take a sip before she spoke again, a knot the size of her fist laying crosswise in her throat. "Brian," she said hoarsely, "let's be serious now. I'm asking you to leave me alone. I've made a new life for myself."

Brian turned toward her. Her eyes were filled with that watchful, removed sort of caution he'd seen earlier in the day when he'd tried to convince her to go out with him. "Casey, I'm back and I want to be with you."

"And what am I supposed to say? That I've been sitting here on pins and needles hoping against hope that you'd return to me? How many times are we going to go over this today?" She began to pace the floor, spilling part of her drink as she went. "I hate to disappoint you but I'm not laying in wait. I've made some major changes in my life, Brian."

"Yes, I know," he said with a tenderness that tore at her senses. "Some of them, no doubt, are more obvious than others." He was studying her body and she realized for the first time that he had noticed her weight loss.

But she could tell that the rest of her words were having no effect. "Forget it," she said with a wild shake of her head. "Let's just forget it all."

"No, I'm not going to forget it, Casey. I can't and I won't. I told you when I left that I'd do anything for you. I meant it, but I'll never forget that I love you."

"But not enough," she railed.

"You don't understand. You never did."

She shook her head again. As he watched her, her hair swung as though it were one solid section, its blond highlights dancing across her cheeks. He wanted to touch her, to hold her for just a moment, but he knew now that she would have nothing to do with him.

"Let's just agree that the past is past and lay it all to rest." She decided that arguing with him and venting her anger was utterly useless. She'd made a whole new life for herself now and the only thing left was for her to prove how she felt by her actions, since her words weren't getting her anywhere.

"Okay. I guess I'm way off base here. Now's not the time," he apologized with a quickness that told her he had been paying more attention than she thought. "I'll say no more about it. Another drink?" He walked toward the bar.

"There's no time, Brian. I'm going out this evening."

"Oh," he said, and then he refilled his drink, walked over and sat down on the sofa, behaving as if he had all the time in the world. He stared at her and then

37

looked out the window. From over his shoulder he said, "Do you remember when we first met?"

"Yes," she said softly.

"I'll never forget it."

Casey gave her shoulders a dramatic shrug and then tried to smile. "I'm surprised." She went to lean against the bar, distancing herself from him as much as she could. "I really thought I had all of the impact of a spot on the rug with you."

"You were very wrong, Casey."

Now her smile became brighter, her composure regained. She would joke with him and end this terribly uncomfortable moment. "How can you say that?" she teased. "The first two times we were around one another you couldn't remember my name."

Abruptly he rose from the couch and took a step toward her. "That's because your name doesn't suit you as well as the one I thought of when I first laid eyes on you."

"Dare I ask?"

"Sunny."

"Sonny?"

"Yeah, as in sunshine."

"Well, that's certainly a catchy one."

Memories were floating over her like a bank of fast-moving clouds, and with each bittersweet memory came the unexpected urge to cry. Reliving old times was doing nothing but harm. Looking down at her watch, Casey frowned. "I really don't want to be rude, Brian, but I have an engagement and I'm running late. I'm afraid I'll have to ask you to drink up."

She waited, taking in the overwhelming sight of him, feeling like she'd been in a train wreck and was battered and bleeding in places she didn't even know she'd had. Thirteen months, four days, and six and a half minutes hadn't been long enough. It should have been forever. The man should have stayed away forever.

"I'll go then." Brian looked around the room, took a big swallow of his drink, and then looked around again, trying to pick up clues. "Are you going with anyone?"

For the briefest instant Casey thought about lying to him. "No. Are you back with your wife?"

"You know better," he replied dryly. "My divorce is final. I started to write you to tell you." His mouth turned down. "That's all behind me now." The thought of what he'd been through made him shake his head. If Casey only knew.

"But you didn't write and you didn't call, did you?" she said with words rolling in sarcasm. *Why am I even bothering to ask this?* she wondered. *Why am I bringing it up as if I had been waiting, pining away beside my telephone?*

"No, I wanted to see you in person. You know how I always felt about talking out our troubles face to face. This was too important to be taken care of in a phone call or a letter, especially after the way we left things between us."

Casey felt a wave of agitation. Why was she letting this mean so much to her? She was weighing each word he spoke as if it were precious gold. How ridiculous of them both to be prying into one another's lives like this when it should mean nothing to either one of them.

With one sweep of her fingers, she pushed a strand

of hair back behind her ear and shook her head, forcing out the swell of emotions she was feeling. "Well," she said, walking toward the door, "as I said, I hate to push you out the door, but . . ."

"Sure," he said, looking at her across the room and then stepping slowly toward the door. He put his drink down on the bar as he went by. "Thanks for the drink."

"You're welcome."

She stood leaning against the door, a shadow falling across her eyes so that he could not see what she was thinking. When he walked by Brian received a drift of fragrance from her as she moved to step backward. When he reached her side he bent slightly forward. Reaching out, his fingertips stroked her cheek.

"Good night, Casey."

Her eyes fluttered once then widened. "Good night yourself," she said softly.

Taking the chance, he bent further down, bringing his lips close to hers before moving slightly forward and pulling her toward him. "Good night again," he whispered as he brushed his lips back and forth against hers, experiencing the special taste that was uniquely hers. He felt her resist, and yet he ignored it, letting his hand move up along the curve of her neck to cup the weight of her head, then gently move forward to press her face closer to his own.

He felt a jolt of sorrow mingle with his passion as his mind strove to figure out how to hold onto this immensely lovable woman whom he'd lost. Then he let his tongue enter her open mouth, touch the sensitive inner recesses in hurried exploration before pulling away. He brushed his lips across hers once more, feeling the temperature rise between them.

At first Casey didn't know what was happening to her and then she felt her body begin to respond. His kiss was like being transported back in time to when they were so desperately in love, and she felt her body betray her, but, taking a deep breath, she pulled away from him and at the same time slowly pushed him away.

"What a wonderful welcome back," he said, bending down to kiss her forehead as he left. "It's all I ever wanted. It's all that's kept me going."

For once the jovial jokester had no response. No words came to mind, only feelings, and they were rushing in, piling one on top of the other in maddening profusion. Casey Clayton was speechless.

CHAPTER THREE

The Vegetarian Village was crowded but the moment she stepped inside she knew her friends from SWITCH were waiting. She could hear them. Amid shouts of birthday wishes and catcalls for being so late, Casey settled herself into the seat at the head of the cloth-covered table and looked at her friends. Not only was she grateful to have them there with her to celebrate her birthday, she was also relieved not to be alone for the evening. She'd do anything to stop herself from dealing with the feelings she was experiencing and from concentrating on the unwanted, unrealistic thoughts she'd been having about Brian.

"Your Virgin Mary isn't as cold as it was twenty minutes ago when it was first served, but nevertheless . . ." Pat McDonald said. The group raised their glasses in salute. "Here's a birthday toast to our dear friend, Casey, who started this group nine months and one hundred pounds ago."

The others joined in. "Here, here."

"And," Angie Robbins said with a giggle that was a close-pitched match to Casey's, "here's to the founder of the finest organization in the entire state of Texas."

When Casey had first begun dieting she had met a

42

woman who worked as a clinical psychologist for one of the local counseling centers. Like most women in modern America, she too was dieting. She had casually mentioned to Casey that sharing experiences was an important thing for an individual to do when going through life-style changes like weight loss.

After mulling the idea over for a couple of days, Casey had started calling around. It wasn't hard to find women to agree to join her. The hard part was finding the right ones—supportive, caring ones. But she'd managed, and SWITCH had been born one Tuesday night right there in Vegetarian Village. SWITCH, Six Women In To Changing Habits. It was a wonderful group, and she often wondered if she could have changed her image without them.

Looking around at her friends as they all sipped their Virgin Marys, Casey thought that she should be on top of the world that night. And if Brian's return hadn't upset her, she would be.

"I'll say this much for you, Casey, aging agrees with you. You look gorgeous. Your eyes are sparkling and your cheeks are rosy. Maybe I should be twenty-eight," Beth Howard teased with a lilt in her voice.

"Beth, it doesn't work that way. You can't step backward," Lynn Clark admonished.

The group roared with laughter. Beth was, at thirty-nine, the oldest member of the group and the one the others looked to for guidance. She also happened to be the psychologist Casey had met many months earlier, only now she was fifteen pounds lighter.

"Oh, I forgot." Beth laughed.

"That's okay, Beth. If I could look like you do I wouldn't care how old I was," Lynn answered.

"Thanks."

"Or like Casey," Heather Rhodes added. "Either one would do."

"Now it's my turn to say thank you," Casey said with a nod of her head. "Of course we have a darned attractive group of women here."

"Are we going to order first or is Casey going to open her presents?" Angie whined, plainly letting all interested listeners know that she was ready to eat.

Lynn Clark spoke up, taking control as she always did. "Casey, why don't you open your presents and then we'll eat. Meanwhile I'll order more Virgin Marys for all of us."

Casey nodded agreeably. While the others giggled as Beth put a large, expensively wrapped gift box on the table, Lynn ordered another round of drinks and Casey took a quick moment to look at each of her friends. Sitting on her right was Angie Robbins, the youngest of the group; called "Munchkin" by her husband and "Magpie" by her friends. The wife of a dentist, Angie spent most of her days watching soap operas and waiting for her husband to come home. She was given to wearing muu-muus and bright big tops that actually did wonders with her dark-brown hair and gold complexion.

Heather Rhodes was an exercise instructor now and had fought the battle of the bulge, choked it down, and stepped on it. Once a week the SWITCH group went to Heather's gym and worked out with her. Like Beth, Heather was a wonderful, supportive woman who after many unfortunate experiences was carving out her own life identity.

Pat McDonald was a happily married school-

44

teacher, with three children, who had lost twelve pounds; she wore a homemade badge to proclaim it. Pat and Angie were best friends and neighbors and always came to the meetings together.

If there was one member of the group who might be considered the fly in the ointment, Casey thought, it would be Lynn Clark. At thirty-eight Lynn was a frustrated wife, married to a successful workaholic who lavished money and gifts upon her but little else. It seemed to Casey that Lynn liked herself so little that it was impossible for her to like anyone else much either. But inside the group there was an almost unspoken agreement that they would love Lynn and exercise patience and understanding with her. At times it was a tougher challenge than losing weight.

Somehow this diverse group of women had formed a cohesive unit, and Casey was extremely proud of every one of them. When their drinks were replenished Casey cleared her throat. "I want to propose my own toast. Raise your glasses, ladies." She waited. "To a group of dear women whom I care for very much." She raised her glass to each of them, one by one. "I drink to you."

"Now then, Casey, open your gift," Lynn demanded.

"Yeah, I'm hungry." Angie handed Casey the present. "This is from all of us at SWITCH."

Hurriedly Casey opened the beautifully wrapped package. "Oh, my gosh," she exclaimed when she looked inside.

"Try it on," Pat said before all of them began to smile and giggle.

Casey looked around the table, a flare of red rising

up her neck and then her cheeks. "Oh, my gosh," she repeated, caught speechless for the second time in one day, a record-setting event.

The others were all laughing and Pat said, "We're all going swimming over at Lynn's pool as soon as she invites us, Casey, and you're going to have to wear that suit."

Casey dangled a black string bikini from her fingertips. Her cheeks darkened. "I don't know that I could."

Nervous laughter broke from the others, all except Beth. "It will be hard at first, Casey, but you can do it." She smiled knowingly. "And when you do it will be a sure sign that reality and self-image have caught up with one another."

Silently Casey said a thank you to Beth. She always understood and somehow found the right words to put everything in its proper perspective. And Casey's new self-image had taken a real beating that day.

"And"—Casey stood up, still holding the skimpy suit—"I may even get the nerve to wear this thing yet. Over my head if nothing else." She began to dance around her chair, the bikini stretched across her forehead like a close-fitting hat.

"As much as I hate to admit it," said Lynn with a tone of weariness in her voice, "since all of you say I usually think only of myself . . ." She glanced around the table. "If I looked as good as you do, Casey, I'd wear the damned thing over the right parts of my anatomy."

"Hooray," Pat called out above the ensuing laughter. "Let's hear it for Lynn. She gave out a compliment."

And for the rest of the night they celebrated, everyone having a good time, even Lynn. Whenever Casey found her mind wandering it went invariably to one topic and she had to steadfastly put herself back on target, focusing in on her friends. She wasn't about to let Brian Powell's return spoil her birthday party or anything else.

The next day she found herself having to repeat the same vow all over again. All night long he'd intruded into her dreams, refusing to go away. She was grateful that she could have the weekend to revitalize her commitment to keep away from him.

Since it was Saturday she decided to give herself a birthday treat. She went to Highland Mall, an enclosed area of shops where she strolled the afternoon away, going from store to store, trying on clothes that would go with her new body.

For her this was a new and exhilarating experience. Her other wardrobe—the one she'd had to shop so carefully for before losing weight—had been selected piece by piece, more for its ability to cover than for its appeal. Now it seemed there was no end to the gorgeous clothes she could buy, no restraints other than those self-imposed ones, like her wallet and her sense of moderation. By late afternoon she'd gifted herself with a pair of stonewashed designer jeans, a pink silk T-shirt, and an expensive white flowing silk caftan embossed with a big pastel hibiscus across the back.

It was late when she returned home. She took off her clothes and showered quickly, washing her hair in the process. Still undressed, she looked into the dressing-room mirror as she passed by. It seemed crazy but she stopped, again surprised by the vaguely familiar reflection. It had been happening again and again lately—her walking by the mirror, abruptly stopping to stare at the body she saw there—a different person, a stranger of sorts. Slowly she lifted one hand skyward, hesitant at first and then stretching up as far as she could. Turning sideways, Casey studied the profiled image before her. Slim hips, full, rounded breasts, smooth, shapely legs, and a jawline that was now lean and sharply defined.

Casey blinked her eyes a couple of times and then looked again, chastising herself for her narcissistic indulgence. For all her pride at seeing the reflection before her, she still harbored a secret fear that what she saw was a grand illusion, a vision created by years of wishing brought to fulfillment.

When, she wondered, was she going to make peace with this new woman? She thought of regaining the lost weight. Returning to the old Casey was a frightening prospect, but at the same time it carried an unexplainable element of comfort. She knew the old Casey. This new woman was an unknown.

Once more she gave herself a hard reflected look. After a moment or two had passed a slow, playful smile began to work its way across Casey's mouth. She smiled at the woman in the mirror.

Hang on, kid, she told herself. I don't know you yet, but I sure like what I see.

With that she picked up her comb, ran it hurriedly through her still-damp hair, and then went to put on her new silk caftan. She'd spend the night getting to know the new Casey Clayton, with a lovely low-calorie gourmet dinner and a chilled glass of light wine.

She turned out the bedroom light and went downstairs to the kitchen, trying to make up her mind whether she wanted chablis or rosé.

Brian Powell felt like a cat burglar or at least what he thought a bungling cat burglar might feel like on his first caper. He stood outside Casey's house, the moonlit shadows drifting across his face. Through the glass of the French door he watched her in the kitchen as she prepared dinner.

He admired her smooth fluid movements as she chopped fresh vegetables. He could hear her singing at the top of her lungs, and he tried to decide if she was expecting company. The way she looked he decided she could be, but the longer he watched, the more he decided she was eating alone. She wasn't putting much food in the wok she was cooking in. He stepped back into the deeper shadows of the trees and walked quietly around to the front of the house. A year ago he could have walked up to the back door and waited to be admitted. Now he'd better try the front door.

When the doorbell rang long and melodic, Casey's first thought was not to answer it. The only people who came to her front door were fast-talking door-to-door salesmen. But when the visitor wouldn't stop ringing the bell she gave up, wiping off her hands with a kitchen towel as she went to the front door.

"Hello, Casey. I was in the neighborhood and thought I'd stop by."

Brian stood on the front brick step wearing his usual affable grin and a freshly starched gray-blue plaid shirt and blue slacks. He didn't look at all as if

49

he'd just happened by, but for the time being she decided to say nothing about it.

"Since I was near here I thought I'd see if your refrigerator was still levitating." He grinned. "I've never seen one do that trick and I figured it might be something we'd want to put in the paper. An interesting article for the Sunday edition."

She leaned against the doorframe, listening, feeling her heart begin to swell. She was glad to see him. There was no denying it but she wished he hadn't come. Then she wouldn't have to think about the way he looked, standing there, waiting to be invited in, so strikingly attractive, every bit as desirable as the first time they'd made love. The rest of her thoughts turned x-rated and she shook her head to clear it.

"You just missed it and I don't think it'll be doing that trick again any time soon. I took the last of the creepy crawly things out."

"Mind if I see for myself?"

Brian didn't know what he'd do if she said no. All he knew was that he'd gone through hell to protect this woman he loved.

Reluctantly she let him in. As she closed the door she sniffed the air. There was a distinct odor of something burning.

"Oh, no," she said, hurrying back into the kitchen.

Brian followed her. "Mind if I join you for a glass of wine?"

"Wine?" How did he know she was drinking wine? she wondered, then she saw how he was staring at the refrigerator. "Really, I can pretty well assure you that levitation time is over."

Brian walked over, opened the refrigerator, studied

50

its contents, and then pulled out the same jug of wine he'd seen her pour from when he'd watched her through the window. He opened one cabinet and then another, looking for a glass.

Casey had watched him out of the corner of her eye and now she turned back to her wok, hurriedly removing the bits of red snapper and green vegetables before they became overcooked. As she worked she reminded herself of a trait of Brian's that she had temporarily forgotten.

The man was a campaigner. He never just did something. He crusaded for it. Once he made up his mind about something he'd barrel his way in, push himself to the limits, do whatever he had to do in order to get what he wanted. She'd seen him do it with the newspaper staff, with her when they'd dated, and long ago she'd decided it was as much a part of him as his five-o'clock shadow.

"You know you're sort of getting to be a regular around here. Is there anything special you're looking for, or is this just the only address you know in Austin?" She left the food on a platter, picked up her wineglass, and brought it to her lips, watching while he tasted his wine.

"This is very good," he said. Over the rim of the glass his eyes met hers. When he spoke again his voice was a mere whisper. "Are you tired of me already?"

Quickly Casey turned toward the cabinets and began taking out a dinner plate. She tried to choose her words very carefully this time. "I don't think tired is the word for it. I thought I explained this to you last night. Evidently I didn't do a very good job."

"I had a real estate agent take me around Austin

today. After seeing your place last night I told him I wanted to find something in an area like yours." Brian sipped from his wineglass again, then smiled over at her, fully intending to ignore what she'd said. He couldn't possibly give up now.

"Oh, really?" she asked, finding herself enormously pleased by the compliment, despite her misgivings at having him drop in on her like this. "And did you?"

"Yes, maybe. There's a house about three blocks from here. It's a low stucco affair with French doors leading out to the back like yours and a small but perfect blue-tiled swimming pool in the back. I'm interested, anyway."

"Brian, I know the one," she said with enthusiasm. "It's over on Rio Bravo. I walk by it every day."

"That's the one. What do you think of it?"

"I think it's a wonderful house from the outside. Sort of large, but beautiful."

"Large enough to raise a family," he threw in. "Remember how we talked about families, Casey?"

No matter what we're talking about, she decided, *no matter what I'm feeling, it always looms between us— the past. And no matter how prepared I think I am, I find myself surprised every single time.*

"You do like to swim, don't you?" he went on. They'd had so little time together before that they hadn't been able to share anything more than their love. There was so much he didn't know about her, so much he wanted the chance to find out. Little things, unimportant things, anything at all as long as it was about the beautiful woman who stood across the room from him, giving him a hard look.

"Brian, if you mention the past again I'm going to throw you out."

"Aye, aye, Captain. Sorry about that. I'll try to keep myself strictly in the present tense," he teased, knowing he'd probably gone too far yet determined to keep testing the waters. "We'll start again. You do like to swim, don't you?"

Swim? Swimming was for fish and so far she'd never found her gills. A wave of embarrassment washed over her when she started to admit she couldn't swim a stroke. She wished she was good at telling little white lies. The skill would come in so handy sometimes. "Doesn't everyone?" she answered, imagining herself thrashing around in his pool, trying to save herself from drowning, but telling herself not to worry. She wouldn't ever have to go there.

Casey set the table for one. She toyed with the idea of asking him to leave, but decided instead to rely on his normally impeccable manners to take the initiative himself when he saw her preparing to eat.

"I didn't plan to come barging in like this and invite myself for dinner," he said, going to the refrigerator and taking out the jug of wine to refill his glass.

He acted as if that was exactly what he'd intended. She went to the refrigerator and took out a bowl of salad she'd made earlier, passing by him without a glance.

"Well then, you'll understand when I don't ask you to stay," she said matter-of-factly, finally facing him.

"Have a heart, Casey. I need someone to talk to. Why don't I just sit here and watch you eat?"

He was playing with her, using that tantalizing grin of his that had always gotten her to laugh. Only this time it wasn't going to work. She didn't want him there. "Afraid not," she answered.

"Let's make a deal," he began. "I promise not to mention the two of us if you'll let me talk to you. I want your opinion on my buying the house and I want to talk about the newspaper. Come on, Casey," he wheedled, still appealing to her good nature.

She stared at him. Was she merely overreacting, or was he deliberately making things hard between them? Why couldn't he have the good sense to leave things as they were? Hadn't he hurt her enough?

There he was, flirting with her in her own kitchen after he'd proven to her that his attitude about love was shallow and superficial. While he'd proven it, he'd hurt her so badly she'd spent an entire year trying to change herself and get over him.

"Brian, why did you come back to Austin? Why not buy a newspaper in Pennsylvania where all your relatives live?"

"The main reason you already know and I promised I wouldn't mention anything about you and me," he answered smoothly. "So for the rest of my answer I will explain that I have left Pennsylvania for good. It's where my ex-wife and all my relatives still live. I wanted to go someplace far away. I've made the break, Casey. This newspaper is strictly my own. That's reason number one."

"What about all the family money? I mean, you're saying you bought this independently?" Perhaps she shouldn't be asking, but at one time they'd cared too much about one another for her not to be curious about his actions now.

"Yes, some of my investments were used to buy it, but it's mine."

She thought of her list of complaints against him. He was still rich, obviously, but not as rich as before, now that he'd bought the paper. Scratch too rich off my list, she thought.

"So, what do you say? Shall I stay for a little while?" he pushed.

Feeling unsure, she nodded. "For a little while," she answered. "We'll eat, talk about the house, and then you'll have to go. Here's your dish," she said, handing him the platter, then turned her attention on the salad.

Watching her pour what looked like a homemade salad dressing over the salad, Brian asked, "What about you? How're you doing for independence? Have you been working on that novel of yours that you always wanted to write?"

She groaned. "Unfortunately, no. What with my job and all I just haven't found the time for a novel. About all I've had time for is work on a short story."

"Hey," Brian replied, "that's a pretty weak excuse. An hour a day would get you started." He watched her put the salad on the table and light two candles, casting a softened glow between them. "I'm going to be putting the pressure on you to get with it, Casey. You're too good at writing to be wasting your talents with the personal column of my newspaper."

"Oh, I don't know about that." She smiled, remembering how supportive Brian had been of her talent.

"Casey, your cat's watching us."

"Oh, that silly Temptation." Casey looked out the kitchen window and saw Temptation's face pressed against the glass. The cat meowed. "She hasn't eaten anything in the last two days."

"I remember Temptation," he said, listening to her meow as he helped himself to some of the fish and vegetables.

Casey grabbed the cat food out of the refrigerator, handed Brian the bowl of salad, and went to the door. "I can't sit down to eat thinking about her out there. She's a strange cat but she's never missed a meal before."

"I bet she'll eat now," Brian said as he listened to the cat's steady meowing.

"Don't let the food get cold, Brian. Go ahead and eat."

"I'll wait," he told her. "Say, I'll bet you didn't know I'm into cooking now too. Seeing your wok makes me want one."

She glanced back at him, thinking of how little she actually knew about Brian Powell. She would have bet he'd never made a piece of toast, let alone stepped foot into a kitchen. She knew he came from an extremely wealthy family, one where cooking was done by the staff.

"What kinds of things do you cook?" she asked as she opened the back door.

"My specialty is barbecue. I can turn anything crispy, charcoal black. You'll have to let me show you some time."

"Here you go, Temptation." Casey started toward the spot on the brick patio where the cat's bowl was kept. The cat dashed past her.

"Hey," Brian called. "She's inside."

"Temptation!" Casey yelled.

"Do you let her get up on the table like that?"

Casey ran back inside the house, watching Temptation's big furry tail swinging from side to side on the kitchen table like some elaborate furry fan. "Get her down!" Casey cried.

With the speed of lightning the cat had jumped on top of the platter and began to eat with bold, greedy bites. Casey ran back inside just as Brian reached over and picked up the cat.

"Ow," he cried, and Casey knew what had happened without asking. Brian grabbed for his hand and Temptation jumped down and scampered back outside, leaving a few pieces of fish on the platter and green beans strewn all over the table.

Slamming the door behind her, Casey hurried over to Brian. "My gosh, I can't believe that cat. She's never done anything like that before. Are you all right?"

"If I can work with only one hand for the rest of my life I'll be fine."

"Let me see." Casey reached out and took his hand into hers, studying three long gashes across Brian's palm that were bleeding profusely. "I'll get something for it." Quickly she grabbed a kitchen towel, soaked it in water, and gave it to him before rushing upstairs for bandages and hydrogen peroxide.

When she came back down, Brian was standing over the sink running cold water on his hand. He grinned at her. "Listen, Florence, I'm going to be all right."

She laughed and went to him, bandaging his hand as efficiently as she could. "I'm so sorry, Brian. I don't know what got into that cat."

"Hunger makes us all do crazy things," he said, longingly eyeing the wrecked table.

"Yeah, I know," Casey answered, putting the final touch on the bandage.

She looked up at him and was reluctantly reminded of the other times when she'd been that close. It seemed like only yesterday.

He was staring at her as though he'd forgotten where he was, his gray eyes full of a mysterious intensity. She felt her face redden.

"There we are. All finished," she said in a choked voice.

He could feel his hand trembling where she had touched him. "No, it's not."

Impulsively he swung his arms around her and pulled her toward him, feeling the softness of the silk fabric press against his chest as he moved slightly to envelop her within his grasp. He couldn't bear to be so close and still so far from her.

He took her into his arms. She saw his moist lips swooping down towards her and she moved her head away. She had to get out of this situation, a situation she'd helped create by allowing him to stay. Whatever happened, she didn't want him to hold her again. It was too painful.

His hand reached up to control her chin and she felt his powerful grip holding her still. She hadn't moved far enough.

His lips sought out hers. When they found her full, soft mouth a warmth surged through him in a swelling display of tension. It was like nothing he'd ever remembered feeling before and nothing he could easily describe. Over and over again as he explored her mouth with his own he marveled at the sensations that rammed his body, making him feel that he had lost all control.

She tried to stop herself, determined that she had changed herself so that she was immune to the tender touch of his hands against her flesh and the power of his kisses. But deep inside her a betrayal was taking place and it was more than mere physical reaction.

It was irrational but he fancied for a few seconds that he was losing himself in the passion of her kiss. It was like being drawn into a whirling vortex of emotion. The sensation of having her arms reach up to cling to his shoulders, having her mouth respond to his with a sensual probing of her tongue drove him to allow his hands to travel down from the curve of her back and over her ribs until he felt the warm undercurve of her breasts, and he let the spread of his hands encompass them.

Then the intensity of his kiss deepened and his hands began to explore each cupped breast and he was on fire, charged by the feel of her flesh beneath the seductive sensations of the silk, and the feel of her was a reminder of how many nights he'd dreamed of holding her like this.

A small, weak voice sang out to her as she let herself be swept along by his provocative embrace. The voice offered up sage bits of advice, clever witticisms she could use to remove herself from the situation, and all sorts of urgings like crosses and skullbones on a bottle of poison, but it had no effect. Casey was responding to the way Brian made her feel as she was telling herself that this must be the final experience.

His forefingers lifted to circle the silk covering her

nipples and she felt the rough texture of his skin as the flesh caught on the silk. She felt her body respond, as if all her nerve endings had met and collected in one spot. There was a sudden, jolting ache somewhere in the darkest part of her and she knew that she now fully understood the deepest meaning of desire, just as she'd come to know with him before.

"Oh, Casey." He moaned. "I'm back and I want to make love to you." Each word he spoke rocked with emotion.

Perhaps if he hadn't referred to his being back, perhaps if the small, weak voice hadn't chosen that particular time to become strong, perhaps she wouldn't have pulled away from him, her mind returning to the present with a jarring urgency that left her numb emotions far behind.

"No," she said in a choked voice. "No!" she repeated, louder this time.

Brian reached for her but she stepped back, her eyes regaining their focus. He held his arm out to her, trying to will her back into his embrace.

"Casey, why?"

"Because," she answered, her voice ragged with emotion.

"Casey, I want it to be like it was before. Tell me you want that too."

"It's been a long time. People change. I've changed." She didn't want to hear any more.

"I haven't changed, at least not in the way I care about you."

"Well, maybe that's why this is wrong. Maybe you should. Remember, you were the one who left," she accused.

Trying to calm her body down, she let her mind drift back to the times they'd shared, a time when she'd been naive beyond her years, too trusting, too easily falling in love with him. The mistake had been hers.

Brian was tall, lean, with observant gray eyes and an affable grin that drove her crazy even before he'd first asked her out. She had been so eager, cheerily optimistic and completely vulnerable, like a newborn. The combination was at first like powerful skyrockets bursting to life and then ending up with a silent, heart-breaking thud.

And now she had a message written in concrete and wrapped around her heart. He hadn't loved her enough.

"Casey, you knew my reasons," he started, remembering back to how he'd tried to protect her, insulate her from the nastiness a trusting, compassionate woman like herself should never be exposed to. "It's been all the hell I told you it would be. I couldn't let you go through that."

"No." She shook her head vehemently, twisting her passion into anger so that she could hold herself away from him. "It's not that you couldn't. You didn't want me with you."

"That's ridiculous, Casey. I loved you. I never stopped loving you, but you didn't deserve to have to suffer what I've been through this year. I was right in not letting you go with me. My ex-wife's lawyers would have ripped you apart in that courtroom."

"How would you know? You didn't give me the chance to find out," she shot back. "The only chance I wanted was to stand and fight with you."

He shook his head in frustration. "Will you ever understand? Will you ever give us a chance to talk about it?"

"No," she concluded, dangerously close to tears. She pulled away from him, her festering anger making her feel weak and sad. She'd allowed him too many chances before he'd left Austin to explain himself. Now, in her vulnerable state, listening to his excuses— ones he'd had thirteen months to improve—would only force her to relive the pain of it all over again.

He watched her move away from him and cross her arms in defiance as she stared at him with those icy green eyes of hers. "What do you want then?" Brian waited.

"I want your friendship."

He ran his fingers through his hair in obvious frustration. "Friendship? I want that too, but more . . . Casey, I want more than that."

"Friendship," she went on in a hard voice. "An employer-employee relationship. None of the above includes embraces, kisses, any intimacies whatsoever. You're welcome back whenever you can come and leave with a handshake and nothing more." She tried to put all the force of her voice behind her words. If he challenged her she was afraid she'd crumble.

"Are you telling me we're through forever?" he asked in disbelief.

"Let's call it as it really is, why don't we? You called us through forever when you left last year."

"You know why I had to leave."

"To this day I'll never understand, Brian."

She couldn't believe she'd let herself fall into this situation again. She was wearing her heart on her sleeve, and there was no reason now. He'd left, she'd started a new life, and she'd never heard from him again until the day he'd sat down on her desk.

"And that's what I'm trying to deal with, Casey, but you're too hardheaded to listen." His frustration grew with every word, threatening to blow sky high. "I had to leave Austin. I had a wife I'd been separated from for eight months who was trying to break up my family's trust, and her lawyers were sniffing all around you and me and everything we were doing. I was trying to protect you, Casey."

She ignored his words. "Friendship. Take it or leave it."

The frigid look in her eyes told him there was no reasoning with her at this point. After a long time he shook his head. "Okay," he agreed with a shrug of his shoulders. "Okay, if that's what you want, that's what you'll get. However you want it, Casey." He gave her a brief nod, then started out the kitchen toward the front door. "However you want it," he called as he left.

Outside Brian started up his car. Usually the smooth response of the Mercedes engine was something he reacted to, but not tonight. Tonight he was still absorbed in Casey and what had taken place between them.

Over the past two days he'd found time to think about her reaction to his return. She'd been hurt when he'd left last year, but she couldn't have been in any greater pain than he had been. Day after day his ex-wife had used every dirty trick available to squeeze one more dollar out of the Powell trust, and no matter how much Casey thought she could have come through it unscathed, only Brian himself knew how terrible it really had been. He'd fought a fierce battle and won, and now it looked like he was caught up in another one, one he couldn't afford to lose.

Brian slowly ran his index finger across his lower lip, remembering how unbelievably soft her lips had felt. In his mind he replayed how her flesh had felt and the way his body had turned electric with her touch.

So she wanted to be friends? His mother had long ago taught him that patience was a virtue. If it was friendship Casey was looking for, friendship she'd get . . . for the time being.

Inside the house Casey hurriedly cleaned up the kitchen, then went stuporously from door to door, checking the locks before going to bed. She still felt Brian's presence in the house. She could hear his voice echoing along the walls.

And her heart still thudded with emotion and her movements were shaky and weak. How close she'd come to succumbing. She'd wanted him as much as he'd professed to want her. But thirteen months was a long time and she wasn't about to let herself forget how much loving could hurt.

"Aeyi yi yi yi yi," she said to herself, trying to joke her way back to sanity as she fought off a hateful wave of pain and longing. Be still my heart.

CHAPTER FOUR

The next day started off no better. The oppressive heat that seemed to originate in Texas and radiate out to all the rest of the world pressed itself against Casey as she stepped outside, and it stayed with her into the office, making her sorry she'd chosen to wear her new black suit.

Brushing a strand of stray hair back away from her face, Casey told herself the reason she was so bothered by the heat was that she'd changed clothes five times before settling on the black suit and it was all Brian's fault. When she'd awakened seconds before the obnoxiously insistent buzzing of her alarm clock began, she'd made up her mind that she'd wear something to work that day that would show off her new figure. Even though she'd sent Brian away, there was no reason for her not to want him to see the new Casey, and it was at that precise moment that the struggle had begun. By the time she'd left for work she'd been positively annoyed with herself. Her closet had been turned into a certifiable disaster area. There were so many clothes strewn around her bed and the floor that she'd have to spend hours straightening what she'd managed to destroy in less than forty-five minutes.

She was angry with herself because all the time she'd spent trying on each outfit she'd been telling herself that it was ridiculous for her to care if he noticed her new figure or not. But her self-talk was a waste of time. She did care. She'd known it from the first instant she'd laid eyes on him, and the way she'd felt when he'd taken her into his arms was like having the knowledge put in writing, signed and sealed. Now she was going to have to figure out how to deal with what was happening to her.

By the time she arrived at work Casey was twenty minutes late. Quietly she eased herself into her cubicle.

"Casey." Brian stood in the hallway of the newspaper office, calling her name at what seemed like the top of his lungs.

Oh, my God, she thought, what on earth could he be screaming for? Warily she poked her head out of her office. "Yes," she answered in her best office voice.

"You haven't been answering the intercom."

Casey bit her tongue, wondering how he'd act after she'd lambasted him last night and wanting to tell him that she'd been a little late to work because she'd been so involved in choosing the proper work attire. "I'm sorry."

"We're having a meeting in my office in five minutes."

"We are?" she asked redundantly.

Did he mean the two of them or the entire staff? Her pulse raced at the idea of being alone with him again. It shouldn't happen but what could she say to her boss?

"Okay, I'll be right there."

Hurriedly she grabbed her purse and rummaged

through it looking for her lipstick. Finding it, she took a broad swipe across her lips with the latest fashion color, Bronze Lover, a bold new shade she'd bought to take the place of her former shimmering pink. Then she generously sprayed the back of her neck with a few squirts of the cologne she carried with her.

When she entered Brian's office and saw that there were several others in the room, she told herself she was relieved. She accepted a cup of coffee from the circulation manager and sat down at the conference table in one of the two empty chairs.

"I smell something," Brian said right before letting out a thunderous sneeze. "Good grief, what is that smell?" he exclaimed, then sneezed twice in noisy succession, causing the shiny buttons on his navy double-breasted suit to stand out.

Andrea Mitchell, the newspaper's society columnist, looked over at Casey and began to fan the air with her hand. "I don't think anyone's told Casey that there's some truth in the old adage about too much of a good thing. Or did you drop the cologne bottle on yourself by accident?"

Casey, face flushed, could hardly bear the smell herself. It hadn't been so bad when she'd given her neck two fast squirts of the cologne, but inside the office with all these people it seemed the odor had intensified.

Quickly she went over to open one of the windows but found she couldn't budge it. "Sorry," she said to the group, as she tried to wrestle the window loose from its newly repainted casing. "I guess the bottle was leaking."

"From one friend to another, next time do us a

favor and come to the meeting *au natural,* why don't you?" Brian walked over and gave the window a hard tap, then raised it easily.

Casey heard the group laughing and she gave Brian a fast look of reproach. He was doing nothing to help her out of an embarrassing situation.

"We'll be having these meetings each morning at this time," Brian told the group. "I look forward to working with all of you again. It's been awhile and I want to tell you a little bit about . . ."

Casey sat back down, listening as he began to explain to the group what his goals were for the newspaper. As he talked she took the opportunity to study him. She watched the way his mouth moved, his smile lighting up his face, his furrowed brows giving added stress to the serious points he was making, but most of all she noticed those eyes of his that seemed so alive they might be able to speak on their own. If she'd expected him to look any different after so long a time she was wrong. He was the same Brian Powell she'd given her love to a year ago, with all his strengths, all his attributes.

Throughout the meeting as he talked to the staff about his goals for the newspaper and the changes he wanted to effect, Brian solicited Casey's opinion, trying to involve her as much as he could without making it look too obvious. He was determined to fall in line with her requests from the night before, and this morning's meeting was a perfect way for him to show her that he could treat her as a friend, exactly as she'd asked him to do.

When it was over, Brian stood at the doorway, speaking individually to each of his employees as they walked out. When it was Casey's time to walk past him, he took her hand into his. "Thank you very much, Casey. I appreciate your input."

She'd had no intention of feeling the way she did when he held her hand inside his. There was nothing personal about it. He was thanking an employee and she was trying to smother feelings of a very different sort. For a moment she felt a sense of déjà vu. It seemed just like yesterday when he'd held her hand so tightly in his.

"Casey, I hope I didn't embarrass you about your cologne. I must be allergic to it," he said.

"I won't wear it again."

"No, don't be silly. It's all right, really. I'll just keep the window open a little. And by the way, I'll say it again, you look terrific."

Casey started to say something but at that moment he looked over her shoulder, dropped her hand, and began speaking to Andrea Mitchell. Casey walked a slow march down the hall back to her office, piqued by a myriad of conflicting emotions.

Brian was behaving just as she'd asked of him. And Casey had to remind herself that she was the one who'd insisted on friendship, as she fought down the urge to resent the casual way Brian was treating her now, no differently than the other employees. One question kept hammering at her: How could he storm back into town, shake her life down to its core, and then so graciously follow her demands? Where was the campaigner, the passionate man? She'd expected him to react very differently.

Still thinking about him, she sat down in her cubicle and absentmindedly reached out to pick a yellowed leaf from the ivy she was barely managing to keep alive on the corner of her desk. Trying to make her little cubicle look respectable was useless and Casey knew it, but she kept on trying. Every piece of furniture in the building looked like it had been used in World War I and then left outside all these years in the rain. Casey's cubicle contained a dull-gray metal desk, an unsteady chair on warped casters, a filing cabinet that responded only when kicked, and one of the first IBM typewriters ever declared to be electric. But the fact that Brian had redecorated his office in record speed and with good taste gave her hope that perhaps he'd eventually redecorate the entire building. She fantasized of how she might help him do it.

But without profits there would be no chance of improving anything, and so Casey set out to work on her column, keeping a sharply critical eye on the way she corrected the ads. As she worked she tried to tell herself that she was pleased with the way Brian was leaving her alone.

That night before her exercise session at Heather's gym, Casey spent almost an hour cleaning up her bedroom, vowing all the while that she wouldn't do anything so foolish again. Despite her best intentions, as she tidied up she kept one eye out for what she could wear to work the next day. As she drove down the Mo-Pac loop toward the gym, Casey played a tape of Melissa Manchester tunes in which each and every one seemed to address unrequited love.

By the time she arrived at Heather's gym she'd made up her mind to do one thing—to stay busy. Apparently she had too much time to think, and thinking

70

was like buying a one-way ticket to aspirin heaven. She promised herself she'd keep the lovely new journal her mother had given her for her birthday, spending more time on writing, a surefire remedy for too much time on one's hands.

The air was muggy hot when she got out of the car and entered Body Beautiful gym, and the icy blast of air conditioning inside was a welcome relief. All of her SWITCH friends were already there, milling about with the other class members in the main exercise room waiting for the session to start.

"Casey, have you worn your new bathing suit yet?" Pat asked the minute she saw her. Pat was wearing a black leotard and her weight-loss button plastered proudly on her chest.

Shaking her head, Casey heard the others start laughing. "But I'm going to . . . very soon," she said.

"Oh, yeah? When?" Angie Robbins challenged her.

"I don't know, but soon."

In the front of the room before a wall full of mirrors Heather was motioning that class was about to begin. Wearing a pink leotard cut in a becoming crisscross fashion, Heather looked like a dream to Casey, with her long slender legs, erect bearing, and the flattest tummy this side of the Mississippi.

And seeing how gorgeous Heather looked, Casey made up her mind to work out a little harder and really put everything into the exercises tonight. It might prove to be the only way to keep her mind solely on her activities.

Then out of the corner of her eye she saw Angie move right next to her, and as she began to breathe deeply in time to the music Casey could feel Angie staring over at her. Angie wasn't going to leave her alone about the bikini bathing suit, she just knew it.

"Okay, girls," Angie stage-whispered to the SWITCH members who stood near one another while Heather led everyone through their warm-up routine of stretches to music. "I think we should all agree to go to Lynn's house for a swim party on Saturday, and Casey will have to wear the suit we gave her."

That was all the others needed to hear. As they swung their arms up over their heads and began to jog in place to the theme song from *Rocky*, they one by one spoke up with suggestions for Saturday.

It wasn't until they had finished most of the routines and had begun to cool down that Casey spoke up, still breathing hard. "Don't you think we ought to ask Lynn? I mean, it's her house."

"Oh, Lynn's such a good sport she won't mind. Will you, Lynn?" Pat asked, with an expression on her face that dared Lynn to refuse them.

Dressed in an expensive new leotard, matching tights, and an armload of gold jewelry, Lynn gave Pat a frosty smile. "Of course not. Although Sunday would be a much better day for me." She turned to Casey then. "You know, you're the only one who thought of asking me. These other ladies have the manners of mountain goats."

"Well la-de-da," Angie answered good-naturedly. "Sunday it is. Okay, girls?" They all agreed, quieting down as Heather led them through demanding floor exercises that required all their attention.

When the class was over, they all stood around in a

72

group talking. Heather joined them when the rest of her students had left.

"What should we bring, Lynn? For snacks, I mean?" Angie asked, always thinking of food.

Beth Howard wiped the sweat from her forehead with her terry-cloth wristband. "Something low-calorie. I've worked too hard this week to blow it all on Sunday."

"In honor of Casey's unveiling I have a new dip recipe." Pat was the one among them who spent the most time scouring out new recipes and passing them on.

"A low-calorie dip?" Lynn asked in disbelief.

"Yes. You take a large container of cottage cheese, mince one small onion, chop up one tomato, then mix all the ingredients together with a package of dry Italian dressing mix. It's yummy with fresh veggies."

"I approve," Angie chimed in.

Casey listened as the others settled on the time for the party. "I feel like I'm being put on display, the way you all keep talking about my unveiling and all."

Her face was pink from embarrassment as much as from the exertion of exercising. This would take some getting used to. Most of her adult life had been spent trying to camouflage her body, not expose it.

Beth gave her a quick hug. "Hey, Casey, let us have a little fun at your expense. You've made it. You've lost all that weight. You look terrific and we all wish we were right where you and Heather are. We're proud."

Casey chuckled. When she heard it put that way she couldn't very well argue. She promised herself that later that night she'd remember the pride in Beth's

73

voice and use it to help keep herself from feeling those old familiar hunger pangs that usually nestled into bed with her and remained until she was fast asleep.

One year earlier it had seemed to Casey that Brian's love was the most potent force ever to have touched her life. His love had made her blossom. Maybe it hadn't made her do it, maybe it had just made it possible for her to blossom, she thought on reflection. But by whatever process she'd come to life—confident, sure of herself, all the things she'd wanted to be. And though there had been a time after he'd left when she wasn't sure she could keep all those characteristics alive inside herself, she had, with the help from her friends and through her own determination. Now she was trying to hold on to her new image.

The days passed so slowly that she thought the weekend would never come. Each morning she dressed with extra care, taking special pains with her hair and makeup as well as her clothes, trying to accustom herself to the look of the new Casey as well as, she was forced to admit, look good for the new boss.

The evenings were the worst time for her. Each night around six o'clock she walked three miles, timing herself so that she took no more than fifteen minutes a mile, then went in to the kitchen and fixed a low-calorie meal, trying her best to stay below four hundred calories. Afterward she would work in the garden or sit outside until the moon was her only source of light.

Late at night she'd take the short story she'd been working on out of her desk drawer and write. One good thing Brian's leaving had done was help her find

74

the time to write. But she wanted to write a novel, a good one, and so far she hadn't been able to find the inspiration to sit down and begin. And with Brian's return she was afraid she might lose what little momentum she had going. As a beginning writer she couldn't function if her life was caving in around her.

When Saturday finally rolled around Casey felt as if she'd suffered through the most frustrating week of her life. It was bad enough to have Brian back in Austin. Having him try to revive their love and then behave as if she were one of his most valued staff members and no more was almost too much. It was a little like being given a box of chocolates, told to eat them all, and then wondering why she had a stomachache a few hours later.

By nine o'clock Saturday morning she'd straightened her house, cut fresh flowers for the kitchen table, and eaten a breakfast of fruit and cereal. She put on her lavender jogging shoes, then took them off again to straighten out the wrinkles in her socks, readjusted them, and next threw on her oldest jogging pants and a paint-spattered T-shirt.

For months Casey had been keeping a food diary and an exercise one as well. She wished that writing her long-awaited book could be as easy as keeping diaries had proven to be. She tried to walk five days a week, attend Heather's exercise class one night a week, and give herself a one day sabbatical to rest.

This morning she began to walk slowly down Rio Street, giving her muscles time to limber up before she picked up speed. Crossing over to Pecan, Casey began making her way to Brazos Street, sensing the unaccustomed weight of tension in her body but recognizing it for what it was.

Her thoughts kept returning to Brian. He was back and he'd wanted to be with her. She'd managed to resist him, and now, after an entire week, she should be extremely pleased with the way she'd handled him. It looked like he wasn't going to be bothering her again.

She stubbed her shoe in a depression in the pavement because she wasn't paying any attention at all to where she was headed. Mumbling to herself she trudged on, picking up speed.

Might as well admit it, Casey. He surprised you. You were the one who said he was a campaigner, an I've-made-up-my-mind-and-by-gum-I-will-succeed sort of man. She gave out a laugh intended to mock herself. *Looks like he didn't want you badly enough. If he did he would have campaigned a lot harder.*

As she neared the house on Brazos she questioned her decision to walk this way, and a spasm of regret turned her feet into concrete blocks. She saw the FOR SALE sign down and wanted to turn around and run but it was much too late. Brian was waving enthusiastically to her from the front porch.

"Hi there," she forced herself to call out, her voice full of false bravado.

"What a sight for sore eyes," Brian yelled, waving her over.

He must be making fun of me, Casey thought. Without makeup, dressed in her old clothes, which fit thirty pounds ago but now hung on her, Casey figured she could give Brian sore eyes just by his looking at her.

"Come in here, Casey. See my new house."

76

She stopped still in her tracks and felt a rivulet of sweat swim down the center of her back. "Your new house?"

He nodded, coming toward her along the sidewalk, a proud grin on his face. As mortified as she felt, Casey still had the wherewithal to notice how handsome Brian looked in his white tennis shorts, stylish polo shirt, and dark leather boaters. She liked the more formal way he dressed each day for work but she thought his casual look gave him a fresher, more relaxed attitude.

"I've wanted to tell you about it ever since I found out that the owners had accepted my bid, but I wasn't sure how you'd like having me in the neighborhood."

He took her arm, ushering her up the steps toward the lacquered double doors of the entrance. All the time he was thinking he couldn't have planned the incident better if he'd tried. Having her walk by was a real stroke of luck.

"You must be teasing me, Brian. I'm happy . . . correction, thrilled for you. I mean, the house is yours, right?"

"Right."

"It's so beautiful."

"I want to show you around. How about now?"

She was making him nervous, he decided, and it had never happened before, not with her. But he had kept himself at a distance from her until he could decide exactly how he would proceed. She was the only person who could make all his pain and suffering go away.

Casey looked down at herself, taking in the baggy

sweatpants that looked like they belonged to a circus clown. "How about giving me a raincheck?"

Nothing could happen between them to make her feel at ease around him. She realized that fact now. She didn't want to be alone with him. His nearness only revived the memory of pain. He didn't seem to be bothered, and his casual ways could mean only one thing—he had never cared as much as he claimed he did.

"Why?" he asked, his disappointment evident. "Because you haven't finished your walk? Come on, I'll go with you, and then we can come back here."

Casey smoothed her hair back from her face, giving up when another strand dropped down along her cheek. Without a comb her efforts were futile. She tried to smile, stalling. "The truth is, Brian, I'd like to wait and come back another time."

He put his arm around her shoulder. "There's no time like the present. Come on in."

With a pride that was touching in its sincerity, Brian showed her through the empty rooms and then outside where there was a shallow swimming pool with wide brick decking all around it. Casey fell in love with the house, the pool, and the entire setting.

"It's one of the most interesting houses I've seen, Brian. No wonder you're so happy with it."

"Happy isn't the word. I couldn't get the papers signed until late yesterday afternoon and I've just now found a mover who'll bring my furniture over from the warehouse tomorrow."

"On Sunday?" Casey asked admiringly.

"Triple time and all the beer they can drink."

"Oh, well."

As if by mutual consent they sat down at the edge of the pool. Casey let her hand run idly through the water.

"I'm going to sleep in my own house tonight. I've checked out of the hotel and borrowed a sleeping bag."

"Sounds like fun." Her thoughts were a thousand miles away, absorbed in how beautiful this big house could be with the proper touches. Like hers, it was Tudor style, built long ago when rooms were large.

"It could be a lot of fun," he said a little too quickly.

It had been on his mind to ask if she wanted to join him, but the instant he was about to say the words, he decided against it. The worst thing about seeing her again was the way his mind kept replaying the scenes of the other night when he'd kissed her. Keeping his mind off holding her in his arms was a little like cleaning out that blasted refrigerator of hers she'd joked so much about. It was a difficult task to accomplish but it was something that had to be done.

He watched her eyeing the pointed roof lines of the house. "Tell me, do you know a good decorator? I think I might need one. My mother always had decorators. Maybe you could help me," he went on. "Tomorrow, especially, when we're bringing the furniture in and arranging it. What do you say? Give a friend a little help?"

"I have other plans."

"Important ones, I guess, huh?"

She thought of her unveiling. "Sort of."

"Is there any way you could see your way clear to change your plans? I admire the way you've made your home so attractive and colorful and I'm a friend who really needs your help," he urged. "Besides, I'll be spending my last dime on the movers."

There was no doubt in her mind that she should refuse him even though the soulful way he kept looking at her with his eyes squinting into the bright morning sun made the prospect seem tempting. Especially when Casey was so certain that she knew how this house should look when it was finished.

"I warn you, Casey. I'm so bad at doing this kind of thing that if you don't help me I'm liable to end up with the waterbed in the dining room."

She grinned, imagining the sight.

"And you'd feel funny coming over here for dinner and eating on a sloshing waterbed." He studied her for a moment. "I mean, coming to dinner when I invite my employees from the paper," he added pointedly.

She let her eyes meet his, thinking about this man who'd broken her heart once before, wondering why she kept inflicting the pain on herself by being around him like this. "No," she said bluntly.

"Why not?" He couldn't figure out what he'd done wrong. It seemed they were doing just fine there for a minute.

"I don't need a reason. Let's just leave it at no."

The hard line of her lips and her stiff, motionless stance told him it would be useless to try to convince her to change her mind. He followed her with his eyes as she rose to leave, wondering what he could do to make things easier between them.

Casey let herself out and slowly retraced her steps home. This time she walked much more slowly than before.

When Sunday morning came Casey went to her chest of drawers and took out the bikini her friends from SWITCH had given her. She fingered the thin straps and the minute wedges of fabric. With a sigh she put the black bikini back in the drawer. She wasn't ready yet, she told herself. Maybe later.

When she arrived at Lynn's house, everyone was out by the pool. When they saw her Angie was the first to tease her.

"Okay, take it off," Angie squealed, referring to the terry-cloth jumpsuit she was wearing. "Everyone's waiting."

Lynn walked out behind her. "Yeah, you're the reason why all this was arranged."

"Your home is lovely, Lynn. So is the pool." Casey looked all around, pretending total concentration on the surroundings. She was already blushing, thinking about what was to come.

"Are you going to let us look at your new birthday suit or not?" Pat called from the table where she was helping herself to the dip.

Casey felt everyone's eyes on her. "No," she said, unbuttoning her jumpsuit and pulling it off her shoulders so that they could all see her old worn-out baggy bathing suit.

"Ohhh." Angie groaned. "I'm disappointed."

"Me too," Pat said.

Heather walked over to Casey's side, looking like a pink dream in a new pale-pink bathing suit that looked molded to her new figure. "That's okay, kid. I know how it is. I couldn't bring myself to wear anything cut below my neckline for a long time."

"We understand, Casey. Another time," Beth told

her as she walked up and gave her a big hug. Beth turned to the others. "We're all taking big steps with our weight. Dealing with our self-image is more complicated than any of us know."

"It's no big deal," Lynn announced, swathing down one perfectly tanned leg with a handful of tanning lotion. "I'm just as glad. Casey might have looked better than me." She straightened up and did a pirouette. "This bathing suit cost two hundred dollars."

"Let's see how it does in the water," Angie announced, and suddenly they were pushing Lynn into the pool and jumping in after her.

Casey stripped off the rest of her jumpsuit and, in her old one-piece bathing suit, she jumped into the shallow end of the pool, laughing with the others. She was no longer uncomfortable.

By the time they'd eaten Pat's new dip, basked in the white-hot sun, and played in the pool it was late afternoon and everyone was leaving. As Casey was going out the door, she promised the others that she'd wear the bikini the next time.

She'd barely had time to change her clothes after arriving home when the doorbell rang.

Brian stood in the doorway, an apologetic smile on his face. "I'm sorry. I know you told me no, but the job's too overwhelming. I need your help."

Casey leaned her head against the door. "Brian, why are you doing this?"

"Look," he pleaded. "It's not what you think. The movers are there. They're ready to bring the stuff in and I don't have the vaguest idea where it all needs to go. I wouldn't ask you if I had any other choice, believe me."

She didn't want to go. She knew she shouldn't, yet she'd never been able to refuse anyone who'd asked for help.

Casey nodded. "All right, but I can only give you an hour. I've had a busy day and I have some things to do tonight."

"I promise I'll have you back in an hour. The movers have been waiting for me to find you. They're as eager as you are to get this job done."

After giving her time to grab her purse, he whisked her out and into his car. Within minutes he was leading her into the huge living room where most of his furniture was being placed. "These gentlemen are ready to move this stuff wherever you recommend. We're waiting for your orders," he told Casey.

There was no more time to lash out at herself for coming to his home. She was suddenly plunged into fast off-the-cuff decisions and rapid-fire planning as she took over.

By early evening all the furniture was arranged and the movers had been paid off. Only the crates of personal items were left to be unpacked.

"Let's take a break and eat. I forgot to eat lunch. Then if it's not asking too much of you, I'd like for you to help me unpack some things for my study. I'll take care of my books later. It'll only take a few more minutes." Brian was already uncorking a bottle of imported white wine. "I bought French bread, salami, and brie. How does that sound?"

She saw him watching her, waiting for some sort of answer. "I'm not hungry but you go ahead."

"You don't know how much I appreciate your help." Brian uncorked the wine and then went to the refrigerator for the cheese and salami.

As he did so Casey walked back through the kitchen and formal dining room down a hallway into the living room where she'd placed a double sofa with two matching armchairs, a coffee table, and two end tables. His furnishings were sparse and eclectic, mostly Danish modern in design, not at all what she'd pictured him having.

"What do you think?" he asked when he brought her the wine.

"About?"

"About the house." He sat down next to her on the sofa.

"I think it's got terrific possibilities. I love it."

"Good."

Casey watched his face, reminded of the good times they'd shared. From the beginning they'd enjoyed one another's company, but their time together had been brief. Perhaps that had been a contributing reason to why they hadn't been able to work things out before.

"You know"—he looked around the living room before heading back to the kitchen—"your furniture would look better in this house than mine does."

She watched him go, his broad shoulders stooped a little as he walked. Was he making a play for her by showing his sensitivity? She resisted the way her mind was following his by picturing how lovely her antique furniture would look inside this room.

Later when they were in the study, a beautiful room with bookcases on three walls, Brian asked her to hold the ladder for him while he put some of his least used books on the top shelves. Each time he climbed to the top of the ladder his hand or his shoulder accidentally grazed her fingers where she was steadying the ladder.

With any other man whom she proclaimed to be "just friends," the occurrence would have passed unnoticed. With Brian, each time they touched, it was like setting off an alarm inside her head, and she felt a fire beginning at the base of her spine and radiating outward in all directions.

"Here's my dictionary," he said as he started up the ladder again. He stopped. "I don't think I'll want it up this high. I use it too often."

"Uh." She cleared her throat before speaking. Her mind had been thirteen months in the past. "I couldn't live without mine."

"Yeah, I used it just the other day to look up a word." He moved back down the ladder and stopped on the bottom rung, bringing one hand up to cover hers, balancing the book with his other.

"That's nice."

"Friendship. Webster has a great deal to say about friendship."

Brian took the final step and put the book down on a nearby table. He turned and stepped toward her. When she moved back, he took another step until she was standing up against the bookshelves, the ladder blocking her on her left and Brian coming toward her from her right with the serenest of expressions on his face. He put one arm around her waist and the other up against the bookcase.

"That's why I think it's perfectly within the boundaries of propriety for one friend to kiss another. Even

Webster classified this as within the boundaries of friendship."

"Now wait a—"

Brian drew in his breath and brought his mouth down to stifle her protest. After a few seconds his tongue parted her mouth in muted pleading, and he pulled her to him with such force that she was left breathless.

She fought him, calling upon all her power to try and push him away. She couldn't budge him. He was holding her too tightly. Instead she felt his breath join hers as he kissed her with a tenderness that began to grow more firm, more insistent with each passing moment. A pool of desire had suddenly wedged itself inside her, and it refused to shrink as Casey brought her hand up to rest against the curve of his throat, her opposition drowning in the strength of his kiss.

If ever I have to die, let me go like this, she said silently to the heavens as his mouth worked its spell upon hers. And then she blocked out all thoughts and gave herself up to sensation, moving her lips in response to his demanding mouth.

Then he moved in meandering slowness down to the pulse point of her neck, his tongue darting in and out, leaving a tiny circle of wetness wherever he stopped. It gave her time to think, time to reconsider what she was doing, knowing it was wrong.

When his mouth caught hers again his kisses were soft and tender, almost worshipful. First his lips caressed her full on the mouth and then he began to press his lips against the outline of her parted mouth, beginning at the center and working his way around and around, over and over again. She kept her hand on his neck, only opening it so that each finger touched some part of him, responding to the delicate kiss with an erotic pull that again made her breathless.

"A friend's kiss, Casey," he whispered through parted lips. "I promise."

The next time his mouth met hers softly, slightly open. Very gently his lips grazed her own, but the suggestion of arousal was somehow more overwhelming than his first kiss. Casey gave out a heartfelt sigh as his tiny kisses drove her deeper and deeper toward surrender.

Brian had made up his mind what he'd do about Casey and this day was to have been his first opportunity for putting the plan into effect. He'd decided that he was going to be her friend while courting her in disguise by appealing to her fun-loving spirit as a way to get her to go out with him.

There was no doubt in his mind that he would win her over. If this plan were to fail—although he told himself he wouldn't let it—he'd simply come up with another and another and another until finally he'd wear her down and then win her. Except he hadn't planned on his losing control and kissing her this way.

"I've got to go, Brian." She managed to gather the internal strength to push him away, wondering why she hadn't tried it sooner. "Really, I do."

When he pulled away she felt an emptiness she'd known from before. She felt his eyes watching her and it was all she could do to keep from throwing herself into his arms. But the man who was now teaching her something about emptiness was the same one who'd taught her about pain, and that was something she no longer wanted.

He allowed her to push him away, aware that he'd overstepped the very bounds he'd established for himself. Yet he couldn't hold himself entirely responsible. Casey was the sort of woman who was unaware of her own sensuality, and that lack of self-knowledge on her part made her doubly exciting. He'd been overwhelmed.

He brought one finger up to trace the line of her lips, wishing he was holding her in the curve of his arms. His fingertip ran softly across the swell of her high cheekbone and on upward to brush ever so tenderly against the down of her eyelashes, causing her to blink. Abruptly he pulled his hand back and stepped aside to let her pass.

He shouldn't have done that . . . kiss her like he had. But damn it all, besides the fact that he was in love with her, he found her utterly irresistible. She made him think and feel a passion that bordered on the uncontrollable.

Brian leaned his head against the ladder and shut his eyes. He'd come back for her and he vowed he'd make her see why he'd left. He'd had two awful choices; one was to have taken her with him, expose her to the cruelty of his ex-wife and her pack of hungry attorneys. He could have allowed Casey to go with him but he couldn't have stood to see what it would have done to her. The only choice he'd thought made any sense was to leave her behind, iron out his problems, and then come back to her, but Casey had never understood.

His dear sweet, honest Casey. He loved her too much to have allowed her to be scandalized and hurt by people who wanted only money. It made no difference that he and Sheila had been legally separated for a year and that she was making time with every available man she could find. What mattered was that Sheila's lawyers would find a way to hurt Casey if he'd allowed her to go with him. How could any man let the woman he loved suffer because of him? He'd chosen to go and suffer alone. It had been the only way.

Casey's feelings were on a springboard, bouncing up and down, back and forth. She'd come close to taking the plunge and yet she knew that would have been a disaster. If she couldn't control her responses then she knew she couldn't stay around him any longer.

When she left his last words echoed in her mind. "Friends, Casey. We can be friends." And his irony did not escape her.

CHAPTER FIVE

"You left me crying in the rain," Casey sang along with a nameless voice on the car radio as she drove to work on Monday morning. "Nothing's ever been the same."

The words seemed true to life as for the hundredth time since yesterday's episode she mentally sifted through her complaints about Brian, trying to secure her defenses like a cavalry officer who's been out-flanked and outmaneuvered. Unable to come to grips with the confusing messages her mind was sending her, she was feeling a little shaky.

First of all, she'd underestimated what his return would do to her, then she'd discounted his effect on her when she'd agreed to go to his house, and now she blamed herself as much as she blamed Brian for what had happened. All she knew at this point was that if he'd never kissed her, she probably could have worked her way into the friendship she had proposed between them. But somehow the intimacy of his kiss had reawakened all the old seductively passionate desires they'd shared. It seemed nothing had changed between them, at least not when his lips enveloped hers.

From the first kiss they'd shared over a year ago,

Casey had been stunned with the sudden awareness of her hormones. They'd taken over, and it seemed no matter how hard she'd struggled to regain control, the slightest touch, a mere brush of his hands and she was like a bowl of fresh whipped cream. And she'd remained that way until the moment he'd left her, with explanations that made no sense, each of them apart, following what each thought was right. Neither of them were able to give an inch toward understanding.

She made herself think of her list of defenses, the ones she had designed after he'd deserted her. She wanted to add to them, but she was too confused, able to come up with nothing. Nothing except her old standbys, the ones she'd conjured up before, like too rich, too attractive, too athletic, and too strong a personality.

And now, in all fairness to him, she'd had to drop off the one about too rich. He was still very wealthy, all right, but since he'd left the moneyed folds of the Powells of Pennsylvania, the too-rich criteria no longer seemed important.

But there was one criterion that did fit—she'd loved him more than he'd loved her. His commitment had never been as great as her own. His attitude toward love had not matched hers. Maybe that was why he could come back and try to pick up the broken threads of their relationship. He hadn't been devastated as she had been.

Already at his office, Brian was sprawled in his high-backed executive chair, looking around the room. As newspaper offices go it wasn't too bad. The carpeting he'd done in a light beige, replacing the worn, somber brown shag. The walls were painted an off-white

91

that would be grimy-looking long before they needed repainting, but he'd had one wall covered with wallpaper in an abstract design. The overhead lighting was typical old office fluorescent, making everything look a little unreal. But the chair was new and from his office window he could see both the state capitol and Town Lake.

Restlessly he stood, stretching his arms high above his head, and then he readjusted his shirt, tucking it inside his slacks with care as if he could rid himself of his despondent mood with the merest adjustment.

He shouldn't be feeling so empty and alone, not when he was embarking upon the first positive thing he'd been able to do in a long time. He was on his own, risking his reputation and his money on making the *Texas Daily* a success, and he should be completely caught up in the project.

But he hadn't planned on the problems he'd faced when he saw Casey again, nor was he prepared for her all-out resistance to him. He had hoped that she would have softened, would have finally seen things his way, known that what he'd done was right. But nothing like that had happened, and he realized he was going to have to work hard to make her care for him again. He'd never stopped loving her, never stopped wanting her, but evidently she didn't feel the same way. After all he'd been through he wondered where he'd find the strength. He clenched his fists in silent determination, then walked over to the personnel files and pulled out the folder on Casey Clayton. The whole time he read through her résumé and background he told himself his plan would have to work. He'd make it work. He *had* to. A man in love couldn't give up.

When he'd finished he put the folder away. Friends she'd wanted to be? The thought made him laugh. Now that he was back he'd never be satisfied with mere friendship, yet he saw friendship as a way to better understanding between them, and he was also aware that the only way to force her to realize that they both wanted more was to play her game. He'd follow her rules . . . for a while . . . as long as he could, anyway.

He leaned back in his chair and clasped his hands over his eyes, then rubbed them. He'd maintain his distance, but he'd call her every night and talk to her about commonplace kinds of things—his new house, the newspaper office, whatever came to mind. After all, that was what friends did. They shared their experiences and their feelings with one another.

And he did just that. On Monday he apologized for the way he'd acted Sunday, and by using all his finesse he'd been able to convince her that it might be all right for him to call her occasionally. He began that evening and continued just as he'd planned, talking and laughing on the telephone, keeping the conversation light and impersonal until he felt her begin to warm to him.

Then on Thursday night he called her and said, "Casey, how about letting me take you on a picnic on Saturday? I've wanted to go to Town Lake ever since I got back to Austin."

She hesitated. So far she'd found it was better to talk to him on the telephone than see him in person. Each day it seemed he was wheedling his way back into her life, slowly but surely bringing the past up to date. "Oh, Brian, I don't . . ."

"Casey, have a heart. I haven't been in Austin for

over a year and I don't have anyone to do these kinds of things with. I wouldn't bother you but I can't stay locked up in the house every weekend like this. And if you're thinking about last Sunday, I promise to be the perfect gentleman."

"No. I don't think so."

"Casey." His voice became firm. "It was your idea to be friends. I'm asking as a friend. Maybe I've asked too many favors of you, but I always thought I could count on you."

"Listen, Brian, it's not a good idea for us to be together. It isn't as easy for me as it seems to be for you."

"I promised you I'd be a perfect gentleman." He listened for her reaction but when there was silence on the line, Brian knew she wasn't going to respond to his attempt to soft-talk her into going.

He drew in his breath and held it for a long time, trying to decide how to convince her. Every contact between them was important. He knew that it was essential for them to be together.

"I thought you agreed we'd be friends," he said softly. "Can't we just go out on a simple picnic? Where is it written that two friends can't go on an innocent picnic? Remember, I'm the new man in town."

"Oh, all right," she agreed, wishing she could take back those words she'd uttered that night in her house. This friendship thing was more than she'd bargained for, but there didn't seem any way for her to wheedle her way out of it. She'd been the one who'd said they should be friends, but now she wondered if her proposal hadn't been a big mistake.

94

"Great. I've been working so hard at the paper I need to get out in the fresh air. I'll rent a bicycle for you and I'll bring our bikes on the back of my car. That way we can have some exercise too. Hey," he said, as though he'd had a split-second thought. "Bring your bathing suit. We'll swim at my house later. See you at ten o'clock sharp."

He hung up and Casey was left with nothing but a buzzing in her ears as she thought about what he'd said. Bicycles? Who'd said anything about bicycles? Bicycles meant agility and skill and . . . and who even knew how to ride a bicycle anymore? Bicycles were for kids. And swimming? In a bathing suit? Who knew how to swim? Oh, no. Absolutely not.

She felt her palms grow clammy, the first sign of her anxiety. Wildly she searched for an excuse to give him for not going. Headache. She could have a sudden, violent headache, one of those kind that made you nauseous. Supposedly that was a popular excuse. A sprain? She could sprain something like an ankle or a wrist. That way she wouldn't have to ride a bicycle or swim but, then again, that would mean pain and she hated pain.

Casey looked down at the phone in her hand. She hadn't even remembered she was still holding it. Quickly she slammed the receiver down. And then she told herself to remain calm. She had over twenty-four hours to come up with something.

By ten o'clock Saturday morning she'd thought up and discarded at least fifty excuses, which, when measured out, equaled more than one excuse per hour of thinking time. When Brian arrived at the door, dressed in another pair of tennis shorts and a pastel-

95

striped short-sleeve polo shirt, she felt her heart sink down to her knees and bound back.

"Uh, Brian, I'm afraid I have bad news. I have to go to see my mother late this afternoon. Uh, she's not feeling too well . . . and so I'll have to try out your new swimming pool another time." She said all that as soon as she opened the door, the words rushing out before he had taken his hand off the doorbell.

Sensing her nervousness, Brian said, "Listen, if you're worried about your mother, we don't have to go on this picnic. Where does she live? I'll take you there right now."

"No, no. It's nothing serious. I just promised her I'd stop by to check on her this afternoon. I hope you're not disappointed," she said as she pulled the front door shut and locked it behind her.

"We've got plenty of other times to swim." Brian took her arm and led her toward his car, which had two formidable-looking bicycles on a back rack. "I'm just glad you still have time to bike ride and picnic."

Casey refused to recognize the panic she was feeling, tightening up her knees so that they wouldn't knock together when she got inside Brian's car. The bicycles he'd brought looked much larger than any she'd ever ridden as a kid. These looked more like small horses. She figured there was a distinct possibility that they bucked too.

"It's been a long time since I've ridden a bicycle," she said as they drove off. "I don't even know if I still can or not." She listened to her own voice, hoping he hadn't heard the same quavering she had.

"You know what they say about bikes. It all comes back to you."

"Ha." Casey laughed before realizing she was being entirely too loud, all because of nervousness.

At a stop light Brian looked over at her for a second, then put his hand on her knee. "Hey, we don't have to ride at all if you don't want to."

She fortified herself with the knowledge that he was offering her an escape, but like a real trooper, Casey immediately decided she'd stand her ground. "No," she answered him, her voice picking up strength as she went along. "We'll ride."

And by the time they arrived at what Brian declared to be a beautiful picnic spot underneath a weeping willow tree on the breezy banks of the lake, Casey had almost convinced herself she could make it. It wasn't until he lifted the bikes off the rack and set hers down in front of her that she felt herself turn sick with anxiety.

"Nothing to it, Casey. Come on. We'll take it nice and slow."

Before she had time to do or say anything Brian was pedaling off. Clumsily she climbed up on the bike and pushed at the pedal with her right foot. The bike began to move and she squeezed her eyes tightly shut for a moment, then pedaled as fast as she could, hoping speed could counteract the lopsided balancing act she was performing from one side of the bike trail to the other.

Brian was already out of sight, something she was grateful for, and after a few minutes her bicycle was less wobbly and she went around the corner, wondering where he could have disappeared to so fast. "Brian," she cried when she saw him.

"I'm okay," he wheezed, leaning up against a heavy

rock boulder that stood near the edge of the bike trail. Blood was flowing from a gash in his cheek.

"What happened?" Casey jumped down from her bicycle right before it went sailing into his. "What on earth happened to you?"

"I guess I was showing off," he answered sheepishly. His bicycle was laying in the grass, the front wheel twisted crazily out of shape. "I took the corner too fast and met this rock formation face to face. The rock won."

"Here, let me see." She threw herself down next to him and gently lifted his face into her hand. There were two scratches around the cut but the cut itself didn't look deep enough to require stitches.

"Something I don't remember if I ever told you about myself. I'm a little accident-prone. Not too much, but sometimes I have troubles like this." He closed his eyes, basking in the pleasure of having her hand touching his face. "I might as well admit it." With his eyes still shut he gave her a sheepish grin. "I'm notorious for these kinds of episodes."

Casey wiped the blood away from his cheek with the hem of her blouse and helped him to his feet. "Let's go back to our picnic spot and I'll come back and get the bicycles."

"Leave them. They'll be all right till we're ready to leave. Right now I think you should hold my face in your lap, pour us a little wine from our picnic hamper, and say nice things to me until I tell you I'm all better."

"You're going to have a nasty mark on your face for a while, I'm afraid," she told him, helping him back to the car.

Okay, okay, okay, she said to herself. *So I've already had to scratch the part about too rich, and now it's time to scratch the part about his being too athletic.* She glanced over at his face and saw his cheek swelling as it turned pale blue and purple. *And I can probably scratch too handsome for a while too.*

Because he was a sick man, Casey followed his instructions to the letter. She took out a blanket he'd brought, spread it out under the willow, brought out the hamper, uncorked the wine and then sat down, waiting patiently while he eased his head into her lap. She took a paper napkin, touched it to the cold wine bottle and then to his cheek.

"Sometimes accidents pay off," Brian teased as they sipped the wine. "How else could I get so close to you?"

"Surely there's an easier way than hurting yourself."

"Then tell me what it is." He grinned, nestling his cheek against the cool napkin she was holding.

It was the first time since his return that Brian had felt any sense of peacefulness, and he closed his eyes, letting himself absorb everything that was happening. Casey was there, holding him. Today she was the old Casey, not fighting him but helping, and it seemed a little like being in the lap of the gods. The summer sun was radiating down on them while a light breeze washed across the lake. Everything was perfect.

After a few seconds he said, "I'm not trying to drum up your sympathy, Casey, but I've got a question to ask you."

"What is it?"

"Don't you ever get lonely? In your house, I mean?

I don't know, maybe it's because it's the first house I've ever owned alone, but sometimes it gets too quiet for me."

"Maybe the place is too big," she replied, not looking at him.

"It won't be. Someday I plan to have kids to fill up the bedrooms. It's a good house for kids, don't you think?"

Their eyes met. "A very good house." She looked away, afraid of what her eyes might be revealing. Then she took a deep breath. "Loneliness is something everyone has to learn to deal with."

"I know we agreed that we were finished but when I came back here, I couldn't help but hope things would be different." He tilted his head upward so that she would have to look at him.

"You mean you didn't expect this?" she asked incredulously. "Well, you should have."

"I knew it was possible. I had hoped, though, that things could be worked out between us and I wouldn't have any reason to be lonely." He stared at her and felt her body tense to his words.

She sucked in her breath. "You made the choice to leave last year without me, Brian. It was your choice," she stated coldly.

"Choice? I'd say I had the choice of the devil or the deep blue sea. I was caught in a no-win proposition, Casey, and you must realize it by now."

But as he spoke he came to a hard realization of his own. She didn't begin to understand what he was talking about.

"Brian," she said angrily, trying to move away from him, but stopping when he brought his arms up around hers. "Did you think you were just going to walk right back into my arms when you'd rejected me like you did?"

Her words shrilled through his mind. "I thought you understood why I left and would love me while I was gone. That's what I thought," he answered angrily.

"That's not the way it works, not when a man doesn't love you enough to let you be with him."

"A man doesn't love you enough?" Her words made him want to shake her until she came to her senses. "Doesn't love you enough," he repeated more slowly. He shook his head. He was the one who'd been all alone, fighting for his freedom, needing to know that she would be waiting for him.

Brian realized more profoundly than ever before that they were coming from two entirely separate points of view, points of view that were so overwhelmingly strong that they wouldn't permit the first inkling of understanding. She was tearing him apart. He loved her, he'd gone back alone and spent almost a year fighting his ex-wife, and only the dream of having Casey gave him the strength to fight.

"When a man loves a woman he protects her. That's what I was trying to do for you," he snapped. "You can't begin to imagine the things that went on in that courtroom and behind the scenes. I'll always be glad I didn't take you with me."

She tried to pull away again, but he was too strong. "Then you must accept the responsibility for breaking us up. Not me. You."

He shook his head. This still was not the time to discuss it with her. She wasn't ready.

101

"I'm not going to argue with you anymore. I'm going to ease my head back down because right now I have a terrific headache. I must have hit my head harder than I thought." He moved his head a little and closed his eyes, dropping his arms from around hers, hoping she wouldn't leave him.

"Brian," she said, noticing how pale he looked around the corners of his mouth. Worry took the place of her anger. "Are you all right? We might need to get you to a doctor. Your face looks terrible."

"No, just let me rest here. I'll be okay."

Brian took three deep breaths as fast as he could, then eased his breathing down slowly. He wanted to go back to the way things were. He wanted to have her hold him and he wanted the arguments, the accusations to be over.

They sat like that for a long time. Casey watched his face closely and was relieved to see that he didn't look as pale as he had earlier. And once her concern had dissipated she looked out over the shimmering water of the lake and let herself enjoy the feelings that his nearness brought her, wishing she could change the past.

"Casey, look at me," he said after a while.

Brian's eyes were on her and he was talking, his finger rubbing against the inner flesh of her wrist. He was staring so hard she was afraid she couldn't match his intensity. The gray in his eyes had darkened like ancient gray stones.

"The times . . . the times that we aren't arguing, are you having fun?"

She sighed, a soft smile breaking across her face,

and then she nodded her head. He raised up on one arm and tenderly cupped her chin into his hand.

"I am too. Sometimes I imagine it's just like the old days."

Ever so gently Brian brushed his lips against hers. He looked at her once more, then brought his face up again and began to send the lightest of kisses against her cheek and back to her lips where with tender insistence he urged her lips to respond to his.

If he was trying to tempt her, he was succeeding. His kisses were so faint that if she hadn't opened her eyes she couldn't have sworn they were real, yet the very tenderness with which they were given seemed more provocative than the most forceful of embraces.

He moved his hand up to allow his fingers to roam through her hair, responding to its softness, weaving his fingers back and forth until he was caught in the tangles he'd created. But before he would allow himself to go any farther he pulled away. He wanted her to want him as much as he wanted her, and he would restrain himself until he was sure she did.

"If I'm going to keep my word that I'll remain a perfect gentleman then it's time for us to go. You need to go and see your mother." Brian wanted to tell her that she was driving him mad with need, but he wouldn't let himself say anything more. She hadn't stopped him from kissing her and that was important right now. He was making progress.

Berating herself not only for allowing his kiss but for responding to it, Casey stood up and began to pack away the picnic things while he went after the bicycles. There was no accounting for what she was doing, letting him kiss her, returning his kiss. There was no justification for it, but the tremor that had rocked through her body the instant he'd touched her still continued to send small shocks ranging all around her, and she felt like a little child playing with her first package of matches.

On the way home the two of them were quiet, listening to music but then Brian turned the radio off. "If we can discount the argument, I don't know when I've enjoyed a day any more than this one with you."

She looked over at him, taking in his coal-black hair and the smooth, clean cut of it. It was hard to believe that this gentle-looking man had been responsible for hurting her so deeply. Then she looked at the purple swelling on his cheek. "How can you say that after your accident?"

He gave her a small smile of amusement that made her grin back in response. "It was worth it."

"You won't say that when you see your face in the mirror."

"Yes, I will. I kissed the woman who rescued me and rested my head in her lap and I say it *was* worth it," he answered dramatically, catching a glance at his cheek in the rearview mirror.

Casey gave out a spurt of laughter, and he listened to that quick bolt of sound and told himself that it was indeed worth it. He always reveled in the fun-loving spirit that was so much a part of her. She made him feel good when she laughed.

"Now I know how you were able to buy the newspaper. You sweet-talked the owners into it, didn't you?"

"That's right and I'm hoping to do the same with you. I mean, be your friend," he added.

She turned to look out the window as they passed the state capitol. Could she be his friend? So far it didn't seem possible. Being around him was like being sentenced to some cruel, mocking form of punishment. He was trying to win her over but she'd never allow it to happen. She'd believed in him the first time. She'd handed over her love and her heart. Once but not twice, she vowed.

"Casey, didn't you tell me that your whole family lived in Austin?" Aware that once more he hadn't stuck closely to his plans, Brian decided to work on the friendship angle again. "I'd really like to meet them," he said.

She laughed again, only this time it was more of a giggle. "My family is about the most eccentric group of people you've ever heard of."

"Tell me about them." He wanted to tell her that he already knew a great deal from reading her personnel file, but he didn't.

"My father is dead. He was a Texas historian who wrote several books about the Texas pioneers. He came from a big ranching family in the Panhandle. My mother owns and manages The Green Chile Ice House on Burnett Road, a place I'm sure you've never heard of."

"Any brothers or sisters?"

"Two sisters, a brother, and a cousin who's like another sister. My mother named all of us girls with names that start with C—Callie, Courtney, Casey. My brother's name is Kirk. Anyway, we're all a little unusual."

"How so?"

"Well, my mother is the original free spirit and she

raised all of us to be the same. The only one she's disappointed in is the oldest child, Callie. The rest of us have proven to be almost as eccentric as our mother."

"It sounds interesting to me. My family has always spent all their time arguing over money."

"And that's something no one in our family seems to pay much attention to, except my father, bless his soul. I guess he worried about all of us so he left everyone enough money in trust funds to make sure we don't starve. My mother says he loved her ways and wanted all of us to be just like her. Somehow I don't know if I believe that or not, but you'd have to meet my mother to understand why I say that."

Brian almost told her he intended to, but thought better of it. All he wanted at this point was information from her. "Someday soon promise me you'll introduce me to some of your family."

"Okay, I will." She nodded, basking in his attentiveness. How could she have let herself forget that Brian was the kind of man who gave his attention so completely to someone?

She wondered if she'd ever meet another man like him. Since he'd left Austin, the other men she had gone out with were nice, staid, reliable men. Just what she'd wanted, or so she'd thought. Now that Brian was back she knew that no man who'd come after him could compare. To give him up was to give up all the passion, all the fire they both lived by.

When they arrived outside her house Casey hopped out of the car, then stuck her head back inside the window. "I had a great time today. Hope you're feeling better."

"I'm glad." He smiled. "And I will. Good-bye, Casey. Take good care of your mother."

Feeling guilty for using her innocent mother as an excuse, Casey got into her car and drove to The Green Chile Ice House. There for the next hour she listened to her mother exuberantly plan on having all her children come for a weekend visit. Too busy thinking about the trouble she'd managed to get herself into, Casey could hardly keep her mind on her mother's plans.

Brian returned to his new house but he couldn't make himself go inside the empty place. Casey should be with him. He wanted her there, and no matter how hard he had to work to get her back, he was determined to have her. He loved her.

But he was going to have to loosen up and he was going to have to avoid any more conversations about their breakup. He'd have to face the facts: She wasn't ready to deal with it. Things were going to have to go slow and easy or else he might lose the tenuous hold he had on the situation. It seemed every time he made progress, he managed to screw things up.

Today he'd done so when he'd mentioned being lonely, and then he knew he shouldn't have kissed her. Thank God he had the good sense to keep the kiss light and not take her in his arms as he'd really wanted to do.

As if he didn't have enough worries to sink a battleship, Brian couldn't help but wonder about Casey's losing so much weight. Was she now interested in playing the field, trying to see whom she could catch? Was that why she'd transformed herself?

He pounded his hand against the steering wheel in frustration. It made no difference. He couldn't lose her, no matter how many other men she might be seeing.

He got out of the car, still thinking of how he could get her to go out with him. Being friends with Casey was proving to be a very difficult thing to do.

When she arrived home her telephone was ringing. She threw her purse down and ran to answer it.

"Hi, Casey, it's me again."

Brian's low, raspy voice vibrated in her ear. Her heart pounded hard inside her chest, reminding her that there was no doubt in her mind that she was walking on hot coals. Mystics could do it and somehow block out the pain, but as uncomfortable as she was feeling, Casey was afraid she wasn't fairing so well.

"Hi."

"How's your mother?"

"She's fine. It was just a headache," Casey lied.

She took note of the raspy intensity of his voice, knowing that there would never be another man whose voice made her long to respond as his did. She felt her heart respond, and it seemed that she had no will of her own. She lowered her head and closed her eyes, listening intently to every word, every nuance of his voice.

"That's good. Say, how about a carnival? It's next Friday and as publisher of the *Texas Daily* I've been asked to attend a VIP ceremony. They just called me."

He laughed. "Ferris wheels, screaming demons, cotton candy— What do you say?"

"Brian, I . . ."

"Why do you always try to put me off when you know I won't take no for an answer?" His words said he was joking but his voice was full of irritation. "Haven't I been the perfect gentleman?"

She tried to laugh. She wanted to match his joking mood, but it was no use.

"No, really. If you promise not to tempt me I promise to be the perfect gent."

"Tempt you?" She knew he expected her to take part in his joking around, but she was tired of all the pretense, all the ambiguous conversations, tired of it all. She wished he'd never come back. She wished she'd never heard his voice again. "I don't know what you mean."

"Just kidding. Trying to show the jokester that I have a little humor too." His voice turned strangely serious. "I'm trying my best to charm you, and you're doing your damnedest to resist."

"Brian, I think it's about time we talked about what we're doing. I don't want to go on seeing you. Why can't you understand that?"

He let her words sink in, sorry because they weren't together, face to face having this conversation. "I do understand, Casey. I understand what you're saying, but I can't accept it. I've come back for you, and I can't let go. Can you understand me?"

"There's no chance for us. None," she declared in a halting voice.

"Casey, when I left here last year I kept thinking that with a little space between us you'd come to your senses. I went back to Pennsylvania to fight my ex-wife over my family trust. She intended to have a big chunk of the money and she'd do anything to get it, including smear your name with the same slime she was trying to use on mine."

"I know. You told me all that," she argued.

"Our separation had gone on for almost eight months before I found out all the dirty tricks she was trying to use on me." He sighed. "And would have gladly used on you."

"It wouldn't have mattered, Brian. Not to me. I loved you enough to go through hell and beyond for you."

"Yes, and that's exactly why I wanted to protect you. How could I let you suffer through all that because of me? It wasn't fair to you."

"And your not calling or writing—was that fair?"

Her words were like a strong blow below the belt. "Don't you think I didn't want to? Every day I thought of you, but Sheila had so many bloodhounds on my trail I didn't think it wise. Letters and taped telephone calls would have served a real purpose for her side in court. I got back here just as soon as I could. I've spent a year of my life in court, what with the delays and all. It's been hell."

Casey felt tears sting her eyes. She'd never understand it. The only thing she understood was that she loved him more than anything else in the world. She'd never stopped loving him, even though she'd tried for a time to fool herself.

"Casey, say something."

There was no answer.

"All right then, please say you'll go with me to the

110

carnival. We can talk then or let me come over now," he urged.

"No," she argued. "I don't want you to come over here."

"Then say you'll go with me." He went on, "If you'll say you'll go with me, I promise I won't bother you again. I'll wait for you to call me. Fair deal?" He'd already decided that Friday night would be the time for him to talk to her face to face. He was getting nowhere on the telephone. On Friday he would make her listen to reason if it was the last thing he ever did.

Finally she shook her head and ran the back of her hand across her lips. She was worn out from all the pressure. "You won't bother me again?" she whispered.

"I promise."

"Very well," she said wearily. "I'll go, but it's the last time. Understood?"

"Casey, that's all I wanted to hear. Sweet dreams. Think of me."

And as if he'd foretold the future, she did. All night long.

CHAPTER SIX

When Friday evening came Casey was prepared. He'd hammered at her, worn her down until she'd agreed to go to the carnival with him; he'd even tried explaining away their problems from a year ago. But that night she was full of resolve. That night would be the end of it all. She'd given him lots of time to prove that their breakup was a mistake. So far she remained unconvinced. A broken-hearted lover was a hard lover to convince, she decided. Nothing he'd done so far had made her forget the torment she'd lived through.

Since the day of his return to Austin she'd been fooling herself, thinking she was over him. The maddening frustration of it all was enough to send her back to her old eating habits, back to the days of vanilla pudding thighs. Well, she wouldn't let herself go back there. She would tell him tonight. There would be no more meetings, for friendship's sake or anything else.

Lately she'd pictured herself going to bed with him. Actually, it was something that had been in her mind for a long time. The dream had always been present but now there was added tension as the frequency of her fantasies increased, as if she were trying to rationalize, to prepare herself for the possibility of it happening in the future.

But she did her best to resist as over and over she told herself no. That would be the final step. The act of passage that would serve as declaration of how much she cared, and that thought alone was enough for her to decide that tonight would be the last night. The end. She couldn't handle it any more.

Even as she made up her mind never to see him again the thought of being with Brian persisted. Always the image was of Casey in the sexy undergarments Aunt Wetonnah had given her. It was a silly image but a vivid one. The scenario played once more inside her mind before she gave her head a vigorous shake to get rid of the entire fantasy.

The sound of the ringing doorbell came as a not-so-gentle reminder that she'd been daydreaming instead of dressing. "Just a minute," she called, and went charging over to the dresser for her underwear. The new jade-green satin bra and panties were on top but she perversely shoved them aside and took out her oldest garments, plain white ones. Hurriedly she threw on the rest of her things and ran downstairs.

"I love your smile," Brian said the moment she opened the front door, and he meant it. Her soft, playful mouth was never more tempting than right then, and as he stepped toward her, the urge to take her into his arms was never more powerful.

"What a nice thing for you to say. Thank you." She turned around to lock the door behind her, trying to ignore his movements. This was no way to start off the evening, especially when she was feeling her vulnerability like an albatross around her neck.

113

"Wait just a minute," he told her.

She was afraid to turn around, afraid of being too close. "What is it?" She kept her back turned away from him, but it did no good. His presence was all around her, all consuming.

"Get your bathing suit." Brian took the key from her hand, unlocked the door, and pushed it open a crack. He'd almost lost his patience with her the other night. He'd nearly accused her of not loving him enough to give him the emotional support he needed when he was away. Now he'd regained his patience. "No excuses tonight. We're going swimming after the carnival. First I'll win you a stuffed animal—the biggest we can find—and then we're going back to my place and swim."

"I don't think . . ."

"No arguments, either. Not tonight." He pushed the door open wider and, with his hand on the small of her back, gently urged her inside. "Get your suit."

It would be best to humor him, she decided, knowing it would be in poor taste to make a federal case out of this. Tonight would be the last night. She'd gotten her resolve back, and she told herself she could do anything as long as she knew tonight was the end of it all. She trudged up the staircase, her heart heavy. The only bathing suit she could wear was the two-piece bikini her friends from SWITCH had given her, because her old one just didn't fit her anymore. She opened the drawer and took out the skimpy pieces of fabric and held them up to the light, her cheeks coloring when she imagined herself wearing it in front of Brian.

"Hurry, Casey. The VIP thing starts in twenty min-

utes," he called to her from the bottom of the staircase.

She gripped the bikini tightly in her hands. Old habits were hard to let die, and she'd spent too long trying
to conceal the way she looked. The idea of exposing
herself between these two miniature scraps of cloth
was enough to make her heart beat like Indian tom-
toms. She didn't know if she could do it or not.

"Casey," he called again. "I really hate to rush you
but . . ."

She ran to her closet, reached for a long caftan she'd
worn around the house before she'd bought her newest
white silk one, grabbed a plastic bag from the top
closet shelf, and plunged back down the stairs, not
knowing how she could carry off the evening with any
sense of composure.

What if he tried to get her to swim in the deep part
of the pool? If she couldn't stand up she might panic.
In the past whenever she'd panicked she'd screamed.
How would he handle a screaming woman? The
thought made her break into a giggle, partly from humor, partly from nervous fear.

"Okay. We're off for a fun night at the carnival and
then to initiate my new pool," Brian said as he led her
to the car.

She started giggling again but stopped herself. He
might mistake her panic for pleasure and he would be
very much mistaken.

The carnival was noisy and crowded and delightful.
As soon as the VIP ceremony was over Brian led
Casey to the Ferris wheel for a smooth, gentle ride.
Once it stopped they raced to the Screaming Demon
but within a short time they both agreed their stom-

achs were taking nosedives down to the end of their toes and then jumping back up. When the ride was half over Casey had tried to scream but felt nothing come out so she'd sat there with her mouth gaping and her eyes filled with excitement. When they finally stepped down, their legs unsteady and their hearts still pounding, they unanimously agreed the Screaming Demon had finished them off as far as any more carnival rides were concerned.

It seemed like old times. Casey declared she'd never had more fun as they'd laughed their way through the evening, and her words had been like music to his ears. Thinking of what the rest of the night might lead to, he smiled down at her and pulled her close. When he'd planned the evening, the chance of merely being near her had seemed enough, but now he wasn't quite so sure. It seemed that no matter what she did, it was enough to make him want to let go of the tight control he'd kept on himself. Tonight was certainly no exception.

He led her to a booth where they threw darts at colorful blown-up balloons, trying to win a live goldfish, and then he spied the booth that held the biggest stuffed animals Casey had ever seen. There were all different kinds and all different colors, none of them very appealing because the colors were too bright or the animals had too strange a look on their faces. But then Casey saw a little girl looking up at a particularly garishly colored teddy bear and she remembered she was looking through the eyes of an adult. To a child they must seem the most wonderful of prizes.

"I'm going to win you one of these," Brian was saying as he took off his sport jacket, handed it to

Casey, and began methodically warming up his pitching arm. "I told you I would and I will."

"How long do you think it will take?" she teased. "I don't think these people have set up this game so that they can give these away very easily." She looked over at two carnival workers, a man and a woman, staring over at them, sizing Brian up.

"Not long. Watch me." He threw three balls at a pyramid of milk bottles and struck only one.

"Should I find a place to sit? This may take longer than you'd planned," she taunted.

Brian turned to her. "See that stuffed Kewpie doll over there, the one with the chubby little cheeks? For some reason it makes me think of you, and so it's the one I'm going to win for you." Brian started throwing again. "I think it's her sweet smile; it's so much like yours I expect her to start to giggle any minute now."

Casey glanced over at the doll he was talking about. It had a cute face, all right, but with a round face, round body, and bulbous legs the doll looked almost distorted. Looking at it triggered off a question in her mind. Was he subtly referring to when she'd been heavy, like the stuffed toy? Was that the way he saw her in his mind's eye?

Anger welled up inside her, clouding her brain. It reminded her of the old Casey, and as unreasonable as it might seem, a reaction had been triggered off inside her. She felt embarrassed and humiliated. For the rest of the time Brian pitched, Casey stood by in silence.

When he'd finally knocked down all the bottles, the carnival worker came over and begrudgingly asked which toy he wanted. Brian turned to Casey. "You choose. Do you want the doll?"

117

She stared at him for an instant, her eyes bright with humiliation. "No."

"Okay. Anything. Choose anything." Brian could feel the tension between them and he'd noticed the fire in her eyes. He tried to recall what might have caused so sudden a reversal.

"The orange teddy bear," she answered, not smiling.

"The lady wants the bright orange bear," he told the man behind the counter.

When he handed it to her, Casey turned around to walk off and saw the same little girl avidly watching her. "Here you go," she said, handing the bear to the child.

"That was a very nice thing for you to do," Brian said when the little girl had run off with the stuffed animal, proudly calling out to her mother about her new possession.

"She really wanted it."

"I know. I don't mind." He walked beside her, willing her to look at him. "What's the matter, Casey?"

"Nothing."

"I can't make things right if I don't know what the problem is."

She shook her head and he watched the way her golden hair moved so smoothly from side to side. He thought back over every word of conversation they'd had since the time he'd picked her up that night, racking his brain for the cause of her abrupt change of mood. A few minutes ago they'd been having the best of times and now she looked like a stormcloud had erupted between the two of them.

He snapped his fingers. "I know. It was the Kewpie

doll with the precious little smile. You didn't like that, did you?" When she didn't answer he took her hand and said, "Come on. We're going to talk this thing out, Casey." Without any more warning he quickly led her out of the carnival and into his car.

"Where are we going?" As time passed, Casey was realizing more and more that she'd made a mistake. She'd responded to some old imaginary embarrassment from a long time ago and it was silly. Her reaction had nothing to do with him, only with how she had once felt about herself.

"We're going to my house."

They rode in silence. While Brian drove, Casey played out the scenario in her head. She'd apologize and then she'd tell him she wasn't seeing him any more.

When they arrived Brian led her inside but not before he'd grabbed up her little plastic bag. In the living room he turned on a single lamp, then turned back to her, shrugging his way out of his sport coat as he did so.

Casey waited for him to say something, ask for an explanation, accuse her of ruining their evening—anything—but he merely looked at her. As the moments ticked by she felt more and more foolish. There was no excuse for her behavior.

He came closer to her then and tipped her face up to his with one gentle hand, his expression open and searching. She closed her eyes, unable to apologize for acting so ridiculous.

"You thought I was making fun of you, didn't you? For some reason you thought I was teasing you."

She didn't answer. Instead she spent the time

119

watching his eyes as they moved across her face. It was as if she could almost tell what he was thinking.

"It's got something to do with the doll." He let his thumb run along the curve of her chin.

She stared at him, knowing she was going to be forced to explain.

Suddenly Brian tapped the palm of his hand up against his forehead. "I've got it," he said with some surprise. "You thought I was comparing you . . . Casey, listen," he began with a whisper. "I'm very happy that you've lost the weight. I'm happy because you're happy. But I can promise you that I thought you were just as sexy, just as appealing before as you are now." His voice softened and he moved his face closer to hers. "Don't you see? I would care for you no matter what. I love you more than life itself. No matter what you do, you'll never be less than perfect to me. That's why I always planned on coming back to try and make things right with you. It's also why I couldn't bear to see you suffering alongside me in that vulgar divorce trial of mine."

Casey could hardly breathe. This man was saying he wanted to love her no matter what she did. The seriousness of his expression, the way he'd said what he had, all of it combined made something click inside her head. She could feel the strength of his convictions.

If Brian felt so strongly that he was right, even now, was there a chance that maybe she hadn't been a hundred percent right herself? After all this time he still felt he'd protected her.

Brian knew dimly, in the back of his mind, that he'd reached her, but he could only hope that she could accept his words as truth. There was more to be explained, but he was afraid she wasn't ready to hear it. Since it was only the first time she'd listened to him for any length of time, he decided it would be better to let things rest between them for a while. "Let's go swimming, Casey."

She nodded but she didn't move, thinking of a phrase—a woman torn between passion and reason. It was a phrase she'd read once in a book. Years later she'd seen it on a movie marquee and the memory of the line had returned and stuck with her. Only now there was real meaning to the words.

Brian tried to pull himself away from her, knowing he should honor the code of friendship, but instead he leaned down and took her into his arms, finding her mouth with his. After a few seconds she returned his kiss, straining against him, and suddenly their tongues were entwined and their mutual desire flamed wordlessly between them. His warm breath filled her throat. Helpless to resist, she raised her arms up around his broad shoulders but did not let them rest there. Instead, caught up in the passion of his kiss, she leaned closer and closer into him.

At last he pulled away and sighed. Hoarsely he said, "Do you want to go swimming?"

Swimming was the last thing she wanted to do then. But Casey couldn't find the words or the thoughts to express anything except her own desire, and she knew she couldn't speak of that so she merely nodded.

Brian adjusted the set of his shoulders as if doing so would make him forget how much he wanted this woman, how desperately his need was announcing itself. "You can change in there," he said more gruffly than he'd intended, as he pointed down the hallway to a bedroom. "I'll change upstairs."

They met outside, at the edge of the pool. Casey had her caftan thrown over her bikini. When she'd changed, she'd steadfastly refused to look at herself in the mirror, hurrying as fast as she could, her mind not so much on how she would look to Brian but returning over and over to the strength of his words and how they'd affected her.

Things had changed between them that night and she knew she was more vulnerable than ever. She'd let her defenses down since he'd talked to her. It seemed she was marching blindly on to whatever would happen between them, willing herself to forget that there would be consequences. She was reverting back to the old Casey, the one who had always lived for today.

When Brian saw the silky caftan she'd covered herself with, he turned around and walked to the outside wall of the house. Without a word he turned off all the outside lights and walked back to her side.

Brian felt he'd never been more attuned to her. She stood there smiling. For the first time since he'd come back she was allowing a little of the real Casey to show, that beautiful, vulnerable Casey, and a surge of excitement couched in passion and desire ran through him with such force he couldn't begin to try to ignore it.

They stood together looking back at the house in the darkness, a lone table lamp casting dim shadows across the open living room and out into the night until it touched the edge of the dark water and reflected outward to the two of them. Never had he felt more certain that what he was doing was right.

He stole a sideways glance at her, took in the delicate tilt of her chin, those high cheekbones he'd compared to cut crystal, as well as the golden shine of her hair. He'd held back for such an impossibly long time that now, as he brought his arm up around her, he was afraid he had crossed the point of no return.

Casey shivered, more from anticipation than from the chill in the night air. She felt Brian's arms wrap around her, pulling her closer to him. In the stillness she could hear him breathing, and as he recognized her shivering and moved her nearer still, she could feel the steady thumping of his heart. It made her want to stay there always, safe in his arms, feeling the very life of him beat rhythmically next to her, but she knew her dream was an impossibility. Tomorrow the spell would be lost again.

Standing back, he said, "Let me help you, Casey." He reached over and took up two edges of the caftan and began to pull it slowly over her head.

She'd never lived through an experience so seemingly innocent yet so sensual, and she sucked in her breath as his fingers managed to touch her in one continuous rising sweep, starting at the curve of her hips where he first grasped the fabric, moving slowly upward to rest momentarily at the indention of her waist and then to run along the bones of her rib cage. When his fingers brushed against the beginning swell of each breast, Casey couldn't tell if it was her imagination or the truth that the backs of each finger hovered there for an interminable moment. She felt each finger move as he turned his hands over once and then began to brush full palm against the fullest curve of each breast

123

until she felt her nipples harden and strain against the thin fabric of her bikini top.

She gasped and closed her eyes while he continued to move the fabric upward, under the smooth flesh of each arm, and finally over her head, where he draped it around her neck and pulled her toward him, a captive inside her own garment. She felt him bend toward her and brush light kisses against her forehead and down her cheeks. Then she felt his lips brush against the edge of her hairline and suddenly his warm moist tongue was inside her ear, moving to trace each curve, missing nothing, his breath echoing inside her brain. Weakened by his advances, she felt her body move against him, urging him to continue his explorations.

She knew that by letting this happen, by responding to her true feelings, she was asking for the pain all over again. Yet she told herself that she would not be denied this last time the touch of his hands, the feel of his embrace. She would know his caress for one final moment.

His control was slipping away from him faster than he'd dreamed possible and Brian knew that this night would mark the end of what he'd managed to restrain so long. He would show her how consumed he was, and in doing so he would also show her what control she held over him, but he would prolong it as long as he could.

"Come on. You've got to initiate my pool. I've tried too hard to get you in here," he said as he abruptly threw the caftan off her shoulders and took her hand inside his.

He took two steps, pulling her with him, and suddenly they were in the water. It felt warm and Casey found herself moving along with him across the water, his powerful hand still holding hers. She paddled her feet, willing herself to stay on top of the water at his side until they reached the far edge of the small pool.

"I'm not letting go of you," he said with a laugh.

"I noticed."

She looked back at where they'd been, unable to believe she'd actually maneuvered herself this far. Then she looked back at him and knew that at this moment she could do anything. He made her feel that way.

The water lapped up against them as they stared into each other's eyes. Brian's gaze was steadfast, his eyes tender and revealing, and she let herself be led by his silent communication.

He marveled at the way she looked through the filtered pool light. Everything about the evening was different. It was special and he knew it. The night seemed to be glowing as if they were all alone in some distant place.

All the world was his and he wanted to share it with her, this magnificent creature with the quick smile and the warm heart. She was all he ever wanted.

Casey felt like she once had when as a little girl she'd been taken to the circus for the first time. Caught up in the show, she'd lived the parts—the acrobat twisting through the air, the brightly costumed ladies swinging high in the sky. All that beautifully delicious excitement was right there in this man's arms and she would be a fool not to revel in it. The moderate Casey would pull away. The old Casey would let herself be caught up and whisked away by the way he made her feel.

Maybe if she hadn't dreamed of such bliss so many times before with Brian she wouldn't have shed her inhibitions so hastily. But she had dreamed of it, over and over again. Like someone craving chocolates, she yearned to share the ultimate experience with him.

Keeping one hand on the pool's edge to keep his head above the water, Brian moved across in front of Casey and kissed her as she leaned her back against the pool wall. She felt the drops of water cascade down both their faces and meld together. A wordless moan sounded deep in his throat and he slid one strong hand over her shoulder and downward until he was cupping her buttocks, moving her against him in the warm buoyancy of the fresh water.

Casey found herself thrilling to his responses as well as her own, and she recognized a tingling sensation in the deepest part of her, trickling upward from her thighs until it controlled her entire being. She gave herself over to the heat of his kiss as she felt her mouth being ravaged by his and his body pressing against hers in the depths of the water, his hand moving her buttocks slowly against the hardness of his own body.

He switched places with her. "Wrap your legs around me, Casey."

She did as he commanded and instantly was gratified with the increased pressure of him against her. At the same time he brought one hand up to tighten his embrace, cupping her head toward his by gently rubbing her neck and pushing his fingers against the spot he'd so lovingly rubbed.

His tongue dueled with hers and he plunged deeper and deeper into the recesses of her mouth as though he could not get enough of her, would never be able to get enough of her. And when she thought she could bear it no longer, he took her tongue into his own mouth, pulling it inside him, sucking hard as if through this kiss alone he might come to possess her as they clung together.

They breathed as one, and Casey recognized a passion she'd dreamed of only one other time, and it had been a deeply repressed desire for the same man. God, how she wanted him.

"There's no one like you." He sighed with ragged breath. He'd recognized it in her before, this giving of herself, this willingness to deal with her own feelings, to go with it, and he knew this was why he'd returned to Austin, to this woman, this woman who had stayed in his heart for so long.

"Come upstairs with me," he urged, and then he began to smile when she buried her face against his neck in a sign he took for agreement.

Breathing in uneven spurts, Brian hoisted himself up out of the water and then leaned down to pull her up after him. When she was standing by his side, he looked down at her, adoration filling his face. He took her into his arms and hugged her to him for the longest time before slowly leading her into the house and up the wooden staircase to his room.

He opened his bedroom door, turned on the light, and took her into a huge room with wood floors and a massive bed covered with a full fur throw. Carefully he shut the door and walked toward the bed, leaving a dripping trail of water behind him. Without disturbing the fur throw, Brian pulled out one pillow and turned around to look at her.

Inflamed with desire, Casey watched him, telling

herself that she must remember each moment of this night, wondering if all men and women could possibly share these same intensely overwhelming feelings. Quickly she turned out the light and, in the darkness, stepped toward Brian, following the path of his wet footprints on the wooden floor, holding her breath as she considered what was about to happen.

She found him with her hands, and when she touched him it was as though both their bodies had united to simulate an electric shock. They stood perfectly still for a time, adjusting to the sensual feel of their wet bodies touching.

He caught his breath raggedly, his mind already spinning ahead to what they would share, and he reached out for her. His mouth encompassed hers then, the gentleness with which he'd kissed her so many times in a conciliatory gesture of friendship now washed forever away by the burning hunger that possessed him.

Her lips opened to welcome him and his tongue darted inside her mouth, reaching out in sensual frenzy, his arms engulfing her. She let her hands roam upward along his shoulders until she found his neck and then she crushed her fingers into his hair, kneading his taut muscles.

His hands began to explore tender flesh, spanning her waist, then gently pushing against the fabric of her bathing suit until he had moved the flimsy fabric down along her hips and away from the softness of her thighs. As he worked to remove the bikini he allowed his hands to explore with loving moves first the swell of her hips, the fine line of her buttocks, and then he ran his hands along the two curves of her buttocks and around until he reached the moist darkness, where he let his fingers dwell in a slow trail of discovery as he longed to know each special part of her.

All the time his lips exerted provocative pressure against her mouth as he made probing sweeps of her tongue, eventually pulling hers inside him once again. She felt a tremor come from him as she stepped out of her bikini while he kept one hand against the moist heat of her as he sought that certain center of her sexuality. She moaned, never having known such exquisite desire, as she lost all sense of reason save the pulsing vibration that he had brought to wakefulness within her.

Trembling, she waited as he grabbed her bikini top and twisted it away from her body. Next, in one swift move, Brian stepped out of his own damp bathing suit. She brought her mouth down to caress his flat nipple and felt him grow hard beneath the warmth of her wet lips, and then she felt him press against her as their bodies tingled with the sudden comprehension that nothing separated them.

He lifted her high on the bed and slid up over her, his mouth meeting hers in one dizzying exploration after another while she felt him melt against her and the tips of her nipples turn instantly rigid as he brushed his naked chest against her own. The erotic contact was enough to make her scream with the force of her desire, and she reached up to pull him to her, letting her hands explore the strong muscles of his legs and upward.

Where flesh touched flesh their bodies were hot with desire, and only occasionally could she feel any remnant of dampness from the pool. And never once had he moved his hand from that private spot of hers, so that by now every nerve in her body was burning to respond to the rhythmic motion his hand had set in tune for her. Her hands reached to explore all of him, wordlessly urging him on, and then he slid both hands down and behind her, digging into the soft flesh of her hips, lifting her body upward to meet his.

Wrapping her arms around his back then, she clung to him, allowing him to fit his body into hers, knowing only that she was desperate to have this man inside her, wanting him more than anything she'd ever wanted before. Quivering and moaning under his loving control, Casey knew then that a tornado could strike, the sky could cave in all around them, the world could come to one climactic end, but she would be fulfilled.

Brian began to move, his body responding to some ancient rhythm, catching hers up with him in a volcanic rise and fall, blood racing, hearts thundering inside their chests, heads swimming with the force of life. They were carried headlong into the vortex of their mounting passion, thrusting deeper and deeper, faster and faster. And when the climax came, it carried them gasping together into a rapture that sent them spiraling outside of themselves to float untethered until the spasms lessened and they could reach out to hold one another until their passion was rested and could return.

And all through the night as she lay there next to him, she told herself not to question, not to concern herself with the consequences tomorrow might bring. Nothing could be as wonderful as being with this man like this.

Once in the early-morning hours when she awoke and found his leg braided through hers and his arms cupped around her as if he would never let her go, she was reminded of that list of hers that she had built so quickly against him. She'd have to scratch her final objection, it seemed—the one about his having too strong a personality. It was strong all right, but understanding too. She reached over and let her fingers caress the tenderness of his lower lip, careful not to awaken him. Her list was shrinking fast, she thought to herself, and then snuggled down further into his arms, wrapping the fur throw around them both, telling herself to treasure each precious second.

She stared up at the ceiling, feeling the tears slide across her cheek and onto the bed. She loved him. She'd never stopped loving him and now she had shared her love for a final time because it seemed that it must end now. They'd settled nothing. They'd disturbed everything. But she had been a willing partner, and now she would have to live with whatever came.

CHAPTER SEVEN

"Casey? Casey, where are you?"

Brian reached out for her but she wasn't there. He knew from the utter silence of the house that she had gone, leaving him alone with only his memories and the remnants of her perfume on his pillow. He brought the pillow up to his face and, with a resoluteness that had only been strengthened by the wondrous night before with Casey, Brian tried to think of what he should do next.

He was frustrated beyond measure, holding on to a string of memories that were being clouded by her rejection of him. But he took heart in knowing that she'd gone to bed with him. She had to have some sort of feeling left for him or she wouldn't have shared his bed.

Everything had to work out the way he wanted it to for them. He knew he'd pull out all the stops, do anything he had to do to make it so. Desperation had taken on new meaning. Even though he'd face a future of loving her more than she loved him, he couldn't lose her ever again.

After a shower and a quick breakfast of a glass of orange juice and a dry piece of toast, he called The

Green Chile Ice House and spoke briefly to Mildred Clayton. Then, following her not-so-clear directions, he drove to her place. As he was going in, he smiled to himself, eager to meet the mother of his beloved Casey, curious about what he'd find.

Inside the Ice House, Brian stood still for a few moments, letting his eyes adjust to the contrast between the sun's glare and the dim interior. He saw a wall filled with bright neon signs announcing the names of different beers. There must have been twenty signs lighting up the wall, and the light cast colored shadows on the tables. On another wall was a bar with a high wooden counter. If a man wanted to lean up against that bar, he'd have to move all the boxes of packaged peanuts, the glass jars filled with huge floating green dill pickles, and the dozen or so potted plants just to find space for his elbows.

From behind the counter stepped a woman Brian instantly assumed was Casey's mother. She had that same playful mouth and a smile that lit up her whole face. He went over to her.

"Mr. Powell, I've been watching for you. I'm Mildred Clayton." She shook his hand, pumping it up and down as if she'd never let it go, smiling all the while.

"I'm glad to meet you, Mrs. Clayton, and pleased that you invited me over." Brian looked around the room, still taking the place in.

"Well, I think it's about time we met. Don't you, Wetonnah?"

Casey's mother turned around and grabbed the hand of a woman about her same age, then pulled her toward them until they were all facing one another. Taking their time, the two women looked Brian up and down as he waited patiently for them to complete their inspection.

After a second look at him Mildred spoke up. "This is my sister, Wetonnah Winslow, Casey's aunt. She's had a hand in raising Casey and I figured you'd want to meet her too. I called Wetonnah and told her to hurry on over here cause she usually doesn't come by until eleven-thirty or so."

Brian listened, thinking to himself that Casey's mother was going to turn out to be a real talker. He shook Mrs. Winslow's dainty hand. "How do you do, Mrs. Winslow? I'm happy to meet both of you."

"We've been wondering if Casey was going to bring you around. We like to meet all the young men she goes out with." Wetonnah spoke up. "We really hoped to meet you last year."

Brian could tell that she was pleased with how carefully she'd emphasized the part about all the young men. She grinned as if she'd said something quite clever.

"That's one of the reasons I'm here, ladies," he told them with a smile on his face. "I want to make sure that there aren't any more young men for you two to meet in the future. I'm here to tell you, Mrs. Clayton, that I'm in love with your daughter."

"Well, I'll be," Mildred said in a quiet voice.

She seemed somewhat taken aback by his getting to the point so quickly, and Brian wondered if he'd underestimated her. From the way Casey had described her he'd imagined she might appreciate his honesty.

Wetonnah leaned toward Brian and whispered conspiratorially, "Our Casey's a real prize."

"That I know," he agreed, waiting to see what Casey's mother would say.

"Let's sit down, why don't we?" Mildred ushered them over to her table.

Casey's aunt sat down on one side of the table. Mildred swung one jeans-clad hip sideways against her chair until it moved enough so that she could sit down and simultaneously shooed away Brian's offer of help. Brian took a seat across from them. He looked from one to the other, very much aware that Mildred hadn't taken her eyes off of him since he'd declared his feelings for Casey.

Wetonnah leaned back in her chair, the picture of contentment. "I knew this was coming. Remember, Mildred"—she gave her sister's hand an easy pat—"I told you my bones said this was Casey's year."

Mildred nodded, never taking her eyes off of Brian once, staring with microscopic intensity. "Why did you come now to tell me this?" she asked with a hint of suspicion in her voice.

"Because I need your help." He looked first at Mildred and then at Wetonnah, his brows furrowed into a deep frown. "I think Casey loves me but because of the problems we had before she doesn't want to admit it. I'd like to see if there's any insight the two of you might give me. I want to know everything there is to know about Casey."

Practically rubbing her hands together, Wetonnah nodded to Brian. "I'm sure we can help you."

Mildred gave one dramatic up and down swing of her head as if to say she'd decided to approve and then began to grin from ear to ear. "Wetonnah's right. After all, who knows Casey better than the two of us?"

she declared with a little shrug. "Would you like a beer?"

After declining her offer, Brian tried to steer the conversation toward finding some of the answers he needed to know about Casey, but it quickly became apparent they couldn't help him. Evidently Casey was a far more private person than he'd imagined. Finally he gave up.

"Now," he said with a sigh and a grin, "tell me about yourselves, your family."

Etiquette said he must stay, and for the next hour the three of them kept up a steady flow of conversation. Brian was captivated by the two women, but by the time he left them there at The Green Chile Ice House, he was more frustrated than when he went in. The only accomplishment he could claim was that now he felt as though he had two allies.

Casey found herself returning again and again to the Friday night spent with Brian not in fact, but in her mind, and yet it all seemed so real, her imagination so vivid that it seemed she was reliving it. Desire—passion—tenderness—all rolled into one. It was something they'd held themselves off from last year, telling themselves they'd wait until the time was perfect and Brian's divorce was final. It seemed depressing that now things had happened so pitifully out of sync.

She remembered how she'd felt that night . . . calm inside and out, like a baby might feel after having been bathed and freshly powdered.

But no matter how perfect the night had been, no matter how strong her love for Brian was, she had to face reality. Her heart was heavy with the knowledge that they'd shared something beautiful together, and it had been like stepping back into the past when everything had been perfect. She made no excuses for herself or what she had done the night before. She hadn't planned it, hadn't consciously wanted it, but when the opportunity came to be in Brian's arms she had taken it and thrilled to each moment he'd held her.

Closer and closer she had come to reliving the memory of their time together one year ago. The present had dissolved into the past, only to become the present again. Yet Casey was profoundly aware that there was no going back in time. Today was today, and nothing had changed between Brian and her except that they had shared a night of passion.

In the cold light of day Brian was still the man who'd left for Pennsylvania telling her that she couldn't go with him nor could he contact her again until his divorce was finalized. Casey could not forget the fact that, in her eyes, Brian hadn't loved her enough. If their situations had been reversed, she believed she would have taken him with her.

After all, they'd done nothing wrong. He had never asked Casey for a date until he had been legally separated for several months. Casey had nothing to hide. She had wanted to be with him. She wanted to share his troubles. She hadn't been afraid of what his ex-wife's bank of lawyers would do.

But now she couldn't think about any of it without recalling what he'd said last night. On the one hand he had professed his love. On the other he'd declared that he still felt he'd done the right thing by leaving her. Something didn't make sense. The puzzle didn't fit together, and it disturbed her.

She couldn't be still, couldn't settle down when she got back from Brian's house, so she began working on her short story. She'd been dragging it out, taking a long time to finish it. As soon as she finished the story, she'd vowed to begin her novel, but she couldn't take on a project of those dimensions until her life was settled.

She heard the telephone ring on and off all day but she refused to answer it. If it was Brian she didn't know what she'd say.

She was going to have to make a decision about her life before she let herself be caught up in something that would break her heart all over again. She didn't want that to happen, couldn't stand up to the emotional ordeal. She knew how it felt, and it was an experience she swore she'd never allow herself again. And how could they ever work things out if Brian still thought he'd done the right thing and she thought she was the one who was correct? Nothing had changed.

At ten o'clock on Sunday evening she finally answered the telephone, tired of listening to it ring. It was Brian. Jovial, full of questions, telling her how he'd called all day Saturday and received no reply, he teased her about her busy social life.

When he hadn't been able to get an answer to his telephoning Brian had driven by her house, wondering if she were out with another man. He couldn't help the insane feelings of jealousy that flooded his thoughts when the possibility struck him. Nor did he feel too much guilt over spying on her.

It hadn't done any good. He saw a light on in her house, which could have meant she was away for the evening or that she was at home. Either way he wasn't

happy. He'd hoped to spend the rest of the weekend—
or some part of it at least—with her, but he told himself he didn't have any right to know about her com-
ings and goings, not yet.

Even as she was telling herself not to become any
more involved with him than she already had, Casey's
heart began to leap as Brian described how wonderful
he'd thought Friday night had been. On and on he
talked about the two of them together, making her
blush. She closed her eyes as he spoke, honest enough
with herself to admit that she was wishing that things
could be different.

And then he changed the subject. "I've been planning a big party to announce my ownership of the
paper, Casey. I'd thought I'd have it in September but
my parents have asked to be included and I couldn't
say no. The only time they can all come is this Thursday. With so little time to prepare, it's going to take all
my attentions this next week to get everything taken
care of. I'll have to hire people to hand deliver the
invitations for this command performance."

"It sounds exciting," she answered unenthusiasti-
cally. She could hardly listen to him for telling herself
not to care about any of his plans. An ache had started
up in her heart the instant she'd heard his voice and
that ache came as the final blow. She was going to
have to stop this relationship before she got hurt all
over again.

"Well, I certainly intend for it to be exciting. I want
my family to meet you."

"You're very kind." She kept her voice noncommit-
tal. Up against his fervor, her resolve was going to
take some work.

"I'm going to be tied up all week, at least in the daytime, Casey, but we have to talk," he said enthusiastically. "We have so much to talk about, like where we're going from here."

She shook her head, fighting back bitter tears. She made up her mind that she wasn't going to answer. Couldn't answer. But he was every bit the campaigner she'd always known him to be. He never gave up.

"When can I see you? It'll have to be late in the evening . . . say, Monday night?"

"No."

"Tuesday, then."

"No."

"Then when, Casey? Honey, this is important—the most important conversation of our lives. Casey, I want to tell you all about the trial, about Sheila, about everything that's happened."

She didn't want to hear any of it. She was so afraid that she might weaken if he gave her even the most feeble excuse. She'd stood up to him too long and steadily she'd felt herself lose ground. "After the party," she finally told him.

"Thursday?" He couldn't believe she wasn't teasing. "I'm going to have to wait until Thursday?"

Casey felt her throat tighten up. "Yes," she said softly. "I'm going to be very busy myself this week, Brian, so we'll have to talk on Thursday. Good luck with your party." She hesitated. "I have to go. Someone's at the door."

She hung up the phone, suddenly feeling that a horde of butterflies was gathering in the pit of her stomach. She knew the feeling came from letting her emotions become reentangled so intricately, and she knew she had to protect herself. She couldn't bear the pain that was coming back to haunt her, even though it was her own doing. The sooner she ended this thing the better off she'd be.

At eleven-thirty that night she was roaming the house in her oldest robe, the blue chenille one with the elbows almost worn through. The robe was her comforter, the one she pulled out whenever things were bad, just like Linus clutched his blanket. She couldn't sleep. She couldn't stop thinking about Brian.

She picked up the phone and dialed Beth's number. Beth always knew what to say to make things seem all in perspective. She let it ring eight times. She dialed Heather's number. Heather was a supportive friend. But Heather's line was busy. Like a drowning swimmer going down for the third and last time, Casey tried her mother. She let it ring once and then hung up, her hand resting on the receiver as she stared vacant-eyed out her kitchen window.

Whom was she kidding? Calling someone else for support wasn't going to solve anything. Not in the long run, anyway. Casey was going to have to dig deep down inside herself. She was the only one she could rely on. No one else would do.

She walked into the kitchen, flicking on the lights as she went. In the old days she would have opened the refrigerator and eaten everything in sight. She walked over to the refrigerator, put her hand on the door handle and opened it, listening to the sucking sound it made as it opened. She peered inside, blinking her eyes at the brightness of the interior light. The refrigerator was full and she was so empty.

With a deep sigh, she began to clean it out, pulling

open the vegetable bin first. Inside were two overripe tomatoes and a mushy head of lettuce with dark-brown edges. She picked them up and carried them over to the trash can under the sink. She came back and picked up three carrots from the bottom of the bin, feeling the lifeless greenery of their tops. Might as well throw them away too. Throw away everything that isn't fresh and healthy.

Working her way through the refrigerator, she picked up enthusiasm as she picked up objects to discard. Cleaning out the refrigerator was a little like cleaning out her own mind, she told herself as she worked. There was no use keeping things around that weren't going to do her any good. She threw out a slimy chicken she'd bought on sale last week. Then she went through everything else until at last she had her refrigerator clean and empty.

And as she worked she made up her mind what she'd do. With Brian around all the time she couldn't begin to think her way through things. His behavior always left her feeling confused and muddled because he appealed to the love she'd never let die yet he never would believe that he was wrong to have left her. She was going to have to tell him and then she was going to have to find a way to leave Austin for a little while. Seeing him every day was unbearable, and what she'd let begin again had to stop. That was the only solution. She slammed the refrigerator door, turned out the light, and went upstairs, telling herself that her plan was a good one.

There was only one little niggling doubt that kept worming its way into her consciousness. Why was it that Brian still felt so certain that he'd done the right thing by leaving her? Over and over in the past she'd fantasized that he'd come back to her, telling her that he'd made a grave mistake, but he still insisted he'd been right. How could it be? She didn't understand his behavior, not when he was back, declaring his love. It didn't make any sense.

The days went by in a blur, not fast but unmemorable. Casey saw Brian only from a distance, he was so immersed in plans for his party, but every day he'd sent her flowers. They arrived shortly after she came home from work and there was always a note attached. The notes said, "Can't wait until Thursday. It seems forever. Brian." She left the flowers untended in her living room, and all week she avoided that room as much as she could.

On Thursday morning Casey went into the office of the personnel man, Hugh Jackson.

"Hugh, I've got a two-week vacation due me," she began. "I hate to ask you on such short notice but is there any way that I could have my vacation now?"

"Now?" Hugh looked surprised and rubbed his nose, a habit of his Casey had often imitated in jest.

"I'll finish all the ads for the week by this afternoon. That way someone would just have to cover for me for next week." She'd purposefully waited this late so that Hugh wouldn't have time to tell Brian. She'd tell him that night at the party, at the same time she told him she didn't want to see him again.

Hugh sighed and got up from his desk. "I—"

"Come on. It's important." Casey knew she could talk him into it. Anyone else on the staff could easily do her job.

"Okay. When are you talking about taking off?"

"Tomorrow."

Hugh nodded, and Casey left his office before he could have time to change his mind. She went back to her cubbyhole to finish her ads for the week.

The final paid ad she corrected was a reminder of her own life:

Sensitive, Single, Optimistic—Woman, 34, seeks intelligent man who is secure in himself and interested in a meaningful relationship. Love outdoor concerts, imported beer and travel. Reply Box 1132, City.

She sat there toying with her pen and finally she wrote one to describe how she felt:

Honest, Loyal to a Fault, Loving—Woman, 28, seeks man with a sense of humor and eclectic interests who can love a woman as much as she loves him and will promise to let her share his good times as well as his bad.

When she finished Casey read it over and wiped away a misguided tear that had managed to find its way down her cheek. And then she wiped another and another. She couldn't help but feel like some gigantic banana split, only she was the one spliced right down the middle.

CHAPTER EIGHT

The cuffs, collar, and front of his evening shirt were so stiffly starched that every time he touched them they made a hollow, tapping sound. With deft moves Brian strung the cufflinks through the starched white cuffs of his shirt and then started tackling the difficult mother-of-pearl buttons. He ran his index finger under his collar, but while it relieved one side of his neck, it merely made the other side itch where it was tightening more. He threw up his hands in exasperation. Everything seemed to be going wrong.

He was running late, mainly because his mother hadn't liked the hotel accommodations he'd made for her and his father. She had suggested, as only a mother could, that Brian move them to the newly renovated Driskill Hotel. By the time he'd gotten the two of them comfortably settled and gotten back to his house, he had less than an hour to dress and get back to the Terryhouse Club where the party was being held.

He stopped what he was doing and marched into the bathroom, swinging cabinet doors open with a vengeance until he found the aspirin bottle. He started to take two, then changed his mind and took three instead. He had a powerful headache.

His headache stemmed from worry. Since Friday night Casey had virtually ignored him. She'd never mentioned the flowers or offered any explanation for his unanswered phone calls. Once he got this damned party out of the way, they were going to have a show-down, he swore as he threw the aspirin bottle back into the cabinet.

The aspirin had no effect. Brian tapped the final button into place and looked over at himself in the mirror. The dark circles under his eyes hardly comple-mented his dark-black hair and he couldn't say much for his spirit either. At a time when he should have cause to celebrate—his ownership of the *Texas Daily* and the oddsmakers predicting its success—he merely felt an unyielding sense of loneliness.

Casey began to dress for the party two hours early. She'd toyed with the idea of not going, then decided she had to attend. She told herself it was something she had to do, something she dreaded immensely but knew she wouldn't forgive herself for if she didn't at-tend. She had some of her pride yet to salvage and she could only do so by doing the right thing. She felt heartsick, fighting against a depression that threatened to engulf her, but she was determined to tell Brian good-bye once and for all.

It seemed to Casey that letting one's feelings come to the surface as she had done two times in succession with Brian was comparable to some ancient bloodlet-ting. She had exposed herself, not once but twice, and now she felt like a slab of raw meat—pounded down, beaten, and bruised.

Her broken dreams lay shattered all around her and there was no one to turn to for help. And the SWITCH meeting the night before had made things seem worse. The group had begun to discuss how women strive for perfection. Immediately the six of them were thrust into a heated debate. Emotions had run high from the beginning of the conversation.

"Men grow bored with women who don't grow with them," Pat had insisted.

Lynn, who always warmed to these kind of discussions, had glared at Pat. Immediately her eyes had flashed with anger, but it seemed to Casey that she'd tried to remain calm, taking the time to smooth down an imaginary wrinkle in her stylish Ultrasuede skirt.

"I don't agree. The men I know are only interested in the way a woman looks."

"My husband says a woman ought to be a good cook first and foremost. He wants me to start teaching our girls how to cook," Angie had said matter-of-factly.

"Believe me, if a woman looks good she doesn't have to be able to cook or do anything else. She doesn't even need a brain," Lynn had argued.

"Oh, Lynn, no," Casey had said, entering the debate after everyone else had spoken up. She'd felt Lynn's opinions were based solely upon her experiences with her own husband, a man she said gave her very little attention.

"What do you think?" Lynn had asked with a wave of sarcasm that dared Casey to have a differing opinion.

"I think that there are men out there who are caring and interested and supportive of women. I think we just need to search them out and then when we find them, be lucky enough to hold onto what we have."

Casey had waited for Lynn to argue, but instead the other woman abruptly changed the topic of conversation and the others followed her lead. Casey had wondered if perhaps her own comments had struck a chord, maybe giving Lynn something to think about.

At any rate, she'd listened to herself speak and as she'd done so, Casey had found her thoughts turning to Brian. Even though theirs was an impossible situation, she'd never deny that he was that rare sort of man who only happens by once in a lifetime.

Since his return to Austin he'd proven himself thoughtful, considerate, an excellent listener, as well as a man who solicited her opinions and then acted on them. He'd breathed excitement into her life, melting down her resistance until she'd finally let all her old feelings reawaken as if they'd never left.

When he'd left her Casey had dated several men who fit the description she'd established in her head as the ideal man—a man of moderation, an unassuming sort of fellow. She'd found plenty of those kind, and all she'd managed so far was unmemorable dates where she'd staved off yawns only by squeezing her jaw hard. With Brian there was never a second left to moderation. But there was pain.

And yet as she had spoken her opinion to her friends she still felt that he was a special man. He'd made her admit to herself that she loved him, that she'd never stopped loving him. But loving him wouldn't make things right. She had fought back the

148

tears that filled her eyes and hastily left the group, their conversation only bringing Brian to life in her mind.

Casey walked up the steps toward the Terryhouse Club, toward the bright lights, the sound of gaiety and Brian. A sense of dark dread made her tense up, and she tried to steel herself for what was to come. That night might be the last time she would ever see Brian Powell. She planned to shake hands with him and walk away from his life and the evening with all the dignity she could gather around her, then she'd take her vacation and decide what she'd do next. She'd already decided that if she couldn't go on seeing him every day she might have to leave Austin. In her mind she'd rehearsed the scene to follow repeatedly.

And as she walked slowly up the brick pathway, she couldn't help but think of what might have been. She'd fantasized before of wearing her delicate new jade-green underwear and of inviting Brian back to her house after the party. Now those fantasies made her feel ridiculously sad. She'd worn the precious underwear her Aunt Wetonnah had given her, but only because it went so well with the elegant green silk jumpsuit she had bought for the party.

The jumpsuit was tailored and fitted, accentuating the new Casey like nothing she'd ever owned. She loved the luxurious rustle of it brushing her skin, and, despite her overwhelming sadness at the turn of events in her life, she was proud, almost shocked by the way she'd looked in the full-length mirror when she'd stopped to put on her gold fluted earrings and had taken a long look at herself. All her dieting had been worth it. She'd never looked better and she knew it.

She stepped inside the entrance, spotting Brian before he saw her. He was standing in a receiving line with some people and he was wearing a stylish black tuxedo, smiling and talking as though nothing in the world could bother him. Steeling herself, she threw back her head and sauntered toward him, holding out her hand, a bright smile of confidence on her face, a feeling of nausea hidden inside.

"Good evening, Brian," she said, not looking directly at him.

"Casey, you look beautiful," he answered, taking her hand and pulling her toward him. He kissed her cheek and watched her jerk away as if she'd been burned.

"Thank you." She looked around, searching for where she should go next.

Seeing her made him know he couldn't wait until the evening was over. "I want to talk to you," he demanded. Suddenly he grabbed her hand and pulled her into a nearby hallway, away from the others.

"What are you doing?" She was too surprised to say anything more.

"Casey, I want to know what's wrong with you. I don't understand what's happened this week."

She tried not to look into his eyes, but he took her chin into his hand and raised it up toward his face. Her heart was racing out of control.

"Please tell me what's wrong." His voice shook with emotion.

"I told you we'd talk, Brian, but not now. You have your party to attend to."

"To hell with my party. I want to know what's bothering you. What's wrong, Casey?"

"What's wrong is I made a mistake."

"What do you mean? You mean with me?" How could she have changed so quickly? he wondered.

"Yes, with you." She raised her eyes up to his defiantly. "Yes."

"Casey, you can't mean this."

Brian stood there looking over at her and she couldn't help but feel that the expression on his face was one of intense pain. She didn't understand how or why but it was there nonetheless.

"I don't want to discuss it now and you have no time, Brian. Let's wait, please." Casey had never intended to begin the evening this way. If he hadn't pushed her she wouldn't have brought any of this up until the evening was over.

"Brian, dear, you have guests waiting."

A woman with Brian's black hair and pearl-white teeth walked toward them. She wore a beautiful beige lace dress and an air of upper-class dignity. She had to be Brian's mother. Coming up behind her was a man who Casey assumed was Brian's father. He was balding and slightly rotund. The hair he did have was thick and curly, white as snow, flowing back from the center of his head to the base of his neck. He smiled exactly like Brian.

"Mother, Dad, I'd like for you to meet Casey Clayton, the very special lady I told you about." Brian took Casey's hand into his for a second, hoping she wouldn't refuse his introduction.

"How do you do." Brian's father beamed.

"Casey. That's a name I've never heard before," Brian's mother said as she eyed Casey.

Casey couldn't help but remember how Brian had talked about his family, giving the impression that they were cool and a little distant. From the aloofness she was seeing in his mother right now she knew what he'd meant.

"Yes, my mother had a gift for dreaming up unusual names," Casey said, trying to be polite.

"Brian, your guests are lining up at the door. I'm afraid they're creating quite a traffic jam, waiting to be greeted by the host."

"I'll be right there," he said stiffly. "Dad, how about entertaining them for a second? Would you do that for me?"

"Of course, son." Brian's father put his hand on Brian's mother's arm and the two of them walked away.

"Casey, promise me you won't leave. I've got to talk to you." He pleaded with her, still holding her hand inside his own.

"Brian," his mother called back.

"Promise me, Casey?" he said, walking back toward his guests, still looking at her as he went. "Promise me."

She stared after him, not knowing what she was going to do. After a few seconds she began looking for the powder room where she thought she could take a moment to gather her thoughts.

Despite her misgivings about the way the evening was going, all she could think of, after seeing Brian and having him touch her, was of what she would be missing once she said good-bye. She hurried down the hallway, knowing that all she'd have to do would be to close her eyes and she could evoke the manly scent of him, the crisp detail of his tuxedo, the clean cut of his hair, and most of all the surprising glimpse of pain she believed she'd seen in his face.

Inside the powder room Casey opened her evening bag and took out a lone tube of lipstick, the bronze shade she'd bought when she'd been conducting an all-out effort to change her image. She went over to the mirrors and began to apply the lipstick, taking her time as she rolled the tube across her already painted lips. What should she do now: leave or stay? She stood there, staring into the mirror for a long time, finally deciding to speak to the people who were there from the newspaper and then leave.

When she left the powder room and made her way back down the hallway, she passed the place where Brian was greeting his guests. Without looking at him, she went into the room reserved for the occasion. Taking a glass of champagne offered by a passing waitress, Casey spoke to some of the people she knew there. The only good thing about the night was the things people were saying to her. From the profusion of compliments she was getting, she knew she'd been right to be confident of the new Casey and the way she looked.

"Casey."

She whipped around, recognizing voices that didn't belong there. Dressed in their finest party dresses, their hair done and loving smiles on their faces, Mildred and Wetonnah stood before her.

"You look beautiful, dear," Wetonnah said proudly. For the life of her Casey couldn't figure out the surprise appearance of her mother and her aunt. "What on earth are you two doing here?"

Brian came up behind the two women and put his arms around them. Motioning for a waiter who brought all of them champagne, Brian helped pass the glasses around to the four of them. Casey gulped down her first one and reached out for another, never taking her eyes off of Brian.

"Casey, I met your mother and your aunt last Saturday. I felt like I'd made instant friends of two of the most interesting women in Austin, Texas, and so I asked them to come to my party tonight." He grinned at Mildred. "And I was pleased when they agreed to be here."

"You two certainly didn't tell me anything about this," Casey complained, feeling left out of things.

"We were going to tell you all about it tonight, dear. Besides, you haven't been answering your telephone."

With her hair puffed into a cloud far more elaborate than her usual style, Mildred looked first at Casey and then at Brian, patting one side of her hair as if to make sure it was still there. Wetonnah was having trouble giving Mildred her attention. Instead she was looking all around the room.

"I see." Casey looked over at Brian, not at all sure of what was going on. Why on earth had Brian taken it upon himself to visit her mother? she wondered. Brian's face was unreadable.

He turned when one of the waiters approached and whispered something to him. "Ladies, I'm going to have to ask you to excuse me. It's time for me to make my little speech thanking everyone for coming. I'll be back as soon as I can."

Mildred nodded and Wetonnah said in a voice much younger than her years, "We'll be waiting right here when you come back."

Casey watched him go. Even from the back, the broad expanse of his shoulders, the way the tuxedo jacket dipped in slightly at the waist, tailored to obvious perfection—even from a distance Brian looked magnificent. He was the sort of man who stayed in one's memory. She knew that there would be nothing she could do to completely eliminate his image. She could only hope that the pain would dim and with it would fade the constant reminder of what might have been.

"I was going to call you, Mother. I've decided to take my two-week vacation. I'm going up to the lake, and I would like to leave the cat with you," she said, then told the two about her plans. She left out any mention of why she was going so suddenly and she was grateful when they didn't ask too many questions. They seemed quite intent on hearing Brian's speech.

"Well," she began, after they'd listened to Brian's opening remarks, "if I'd known that the two of you were going to be here I'd have made plans to stay, but I'm going to have to run." She started to give her mother a quick peck on the cheek just as Brian was about to end his speech.

"Run? You mean you're leaving?" Mildred declared.

"Yes."

"Oh, Casey, you can't just leave Bri—uh, Mr. Powell's party. Not now."

Casey's mouth almost fell open. Brian? How well do they know him? she fumed. I'm going to have a talk

155

with my mother when all of this is over, Casey promised herself, a nice long talk. She looked over at her mother's adoring face. Somehow Brian had met them and seemingly won them over.

She saw Hugh Jackson go up to Brian and shake his hand, talking all the time. She wondered if Hugh had told Brian about her vacation and when she saw Brian's eyes following her from across the room, she was afraid he was telling him right then.

The pressure was piling like slabs of stone on top of her, and it suddenly seemed that the enormity of the evening was more than Casey could bear. Things were very different from what she'd planned. Blinking back tears, she turned back to Wetonnah. "Yes, I really have to go. I have a date."

"A date?" Mildred echoed.

"Yes, and I'm afraid I'm going to be late," she lied, ashamed that she'd been reduced to lying to her own family. "Have a wonderful night." With a hasty kiss Casey left them and began to worm her way through the crowd of people toward the front door.

As Brian finished his thanks he saw one of the butlers holding the door open for Casey and then he saw her disappear through it. Without looking at them he shook the hands of those around him and hurried toward where he'd last seen her.

Quickly Casey made her way to her car. She wasn't ready to say good-bye to Brian. Maybe she'd write to him; maybe in writing she could say what she couldn't find the words for now.

"Casey, stop," Brian demanded as he chased her. "Stop."

She turned, her hand on the door of her car. She'd almost made it without having to face him.

"What are you doing? What in God's name is the matter with you?" he shouted, blindingly angry.

"I have to go, Brian." Her eyes darted around but there was no one else outside and no chance of an interruption. "I'm sorry."

"You're sorry," he spat. "Sorry? Is that all you can say to me? Hugh tells me you're leaving for a little vacation." His hands were knotted into fists, his jaw quivered with undiluted rage.

"Yes . . . I've decided—" she began, but found she couldn't finish.

"Why?" He reached out and clamped his hand down on top of hers so that she couldn't open the car door. "Why?"

"I need to get away, Brian." She looked down at his hand on top of hers and then up at his eyes, which were stone-hard gray. "I've decided . . . I've decided not to see you any more."

"What?" he yelled. "You've got to be kidding."

"No, I'm not," she said softly. The price of her words lay heavy on her heart. She didn't want to have to tell him that, just as she hadn't wanted to say good-bye last year.

"Casey, I'm not going to accept this." He raised his hands up toward her face, then dropped them down to her shoulders and began to shake her. "Do you understand me? I'm not."

"Oh, Brian, why don't you give it up?" she begged.

The pain in his voice matched that of her own feelings and she found herself wondering how it could be

157

that they were standing there hurting one another as they were. What cruel designs love could draw.

"Give up on you?" he exploded, his mouth twisted in anger, his hands pushing and pulling against her arms again.

She nodded, hating to see the tormented look in his eyes. "Whatever we had is finished. You killed it."

"How? How do you give up on somebody you love, Casey? You tell me. . . ."

"I don't know. I thought you were the expert in that field."

"That's what you did, wasn't it?" His hands stopped moving and held her tight. "You didn't understand what I was trying to tell you last year so you gave up on me. I always wondered how you could do that."

She looked perplexed. "No, it wasn't like that at all, Brian."

"Well, good. I'd like you to explain it all to me because I never gave up on you. Not even when I heard you say you never wanted to see me again. I never gave up."

"You're trying to make it sound like I was the one who didn't care enough in the relationship."

"Because it's true. You let your emotions blind you so badly that you decided you'd rather give up our love than send me off with your good wishes to help me through my hardships." His voice twisted with each word.

Her eyes widened in surprise. She watched him as he took a step back from her, his body shaking with rage. How could he possibly believe what he was saying?

"It wasn't bad enough that I had to go through the trial and give up a big part of my family's money in order to squelch that she-cat of an ex-wife of mine. Oh, no." He gave his head a vehement shake. "I had to go back knowing that the woman I loved hadn't loved me enough to trust my judgment."

She took a step toward him. Her mind was whirling with his words and she was too astounded to say anything. How could he have thought that she hadn't loved him enough? How dare he reproach her?

She gasped. "How dare you? You left me so deeply hurt I didn't know if I'd ever get over it. I changed my entire life because of you. I had to forget you."

"But I never stopped loving you, Casey. That's why I came back. And I'll go on loving you," he cried, and tightening up his fist, he hit the hood of her car.

The thudding sound of his flesh hitting metal startled her into action. She couldn't think, couldn't breathe. She opened the car door and jumped inside. Shouting at one another would do neither of them any good.

"Casey, we're not finished!" Brian yelled as she drove away, but she knew that they were, for the time being at least. All her reasoning, all her rational ways were gone, and there was only the thought that she loved him with all her might.

But loving and having were two different things. They were two different people standing across a chasm looking out to one another. Words couldn't bring them together, only understanding.

She blinked back tears, wondering what had happened that had suddenly made his vulnerability so apparent to her. Whatever it was, she knew that if she'd

159

stayed there for one more second, she'd have gone to him and begged him for his love and his forgiveness. It made no sense. He should be the one asking for forgiveness, not her.

CHAPTER NINE

"Damn it, Casey, open this door."

She stood on the staircase, caught halfway between the first and second story. She'd been home only long enough to throw a few of her things into a suitcase and to find Temptation. Now she stood, the cat's carrying case in one hand, her suitcase in the other, and her purse slung over her shoulder.

Brian was beating on the front door, trying to get inside. How he'd managed to excuse himself from his own party she didn't even want to think about. Nevertheless, he was there, pounding his fists in unrelenting anger, shouting at the top of his lungs.

She held her breath, willing him away. They were both too explosive, too close to being out of control. He'd caught her off-guard with his attack on her. He'd made her feel defenseless, unable to think.

For the life of her, Casey couldn't understand, couldn't believe that Brian's views of how they'd parted were so different from hers. It didn't seem possible.

She tried to tell herself that she didn't want to hear any more of his side of the story. Everything that could be said already had been and the sensible thing to do would be to let it all die down without any more rhetoric between them. They were fighting old passions.

"Casey," Brian roared, "if you don't unlock this door, I'll break it down! To the count of ten," he yelled, raising his voice even louder. "One . . . two . . . three!"

His violent beating on the wooden door said he wasn't going to give up so she went down the stairs, put her suitcase down by the entrance, and with hands that refused to stop shaking unlocked the bolt. The sight of him, eyes cold, jaw locked with anger, was a powerful experience.

"Damn it, Casey, you ruined my party."

His voice was a combination of smooth velvet and scratching sandpaper, as disturbing as his look. "Go back to your party," she said, wishing he'd never come. Her mind was acknowledging the twinges of foreboding that licked at the edges of her consciousness.

"No. Tonight is the night you and I settle things between us. I've tried the friendship route. I've exercised patience. I've done everything I know of and nothing's worked with you. I've had it."

"There's nothing to settle," she snapped back.

"Like hell there's not." With that he charged inside the house, leaving her no choice but to step aside or be run over.

He spun around to look at her. In some magnetic way his eyes suddenly held hers. She watched the hard stone look of them take on a chameleonlike change. They became warm and compelling, making it impossible for her to look away.

Brian leaned up against the door he'd tried to cave in with his fists and drew a deep sigh, speaking her name as he expelled his breath. "Casey. Casey," he repeated softly.

Reaching out for her, Brian drew Casey to him. Steadfastly ignoring the way she was shaking her head back and forth, he let his lips overtake hers. He couldn't stop himself any more than he could fly.

"No, Brian," she murmured when she realized what was happening to her, but her words only allowed him to gain fuller access to her open mouth. She felt that moist heat was being transferred as his lips applied unrelenting pressure against her own.

Taking his time, Brian brought his arms up to encircle her, letting himself relax for a fractional moment as he held her in his arms. How long would it be before she began a major resistance? he wondered.

He nuzzled the side of her head and inhaled the flowery fragrance of her hair and skin, a fragrance that was so much a part of her. When he felt her pulling away from him he let her go without hesitation. It was going to be a long night.

The night would be long because when he'd left his party he'd vowed that he would make Casey tell him she loved him. He had to hear her say it aloud, knowing that they could not go on like this, hurting each other, hurting themselves.

It was all too obvious that Casey was trying to hold herself back. She was doing everything she could do to deny her feelings. The only thing that had kept him going this far was the belief that no matter what she said or did, she loved him. Perhaps she didn't love him as much as he loved her, but he'd take what he could get. He loved her enough for both of them.

"Brian, this is senseless. I wish you'd leave."

"No such luck," he declared emphatically.

"Please."

"Casey, we left our conversation unfinished. Don't you think we owe it to one another to talk things over?"

Lost in the crazed way his kiss had made her body react, she couldn't find the right words to make him understand. "I think the best thing for us to do is stop talking."

Ignoring her, he walked into the darkened living room and flicked on the light switch. "Your flowers are dying from what looks like neglect." With his fingertips he crushed a dead flower and let the crackling dry petals fall to the tabletop.

"Brian," she said, following him into the living room. "Whatever it is you've come to say, say it and let's get it over with."

There was a certain weariness in the way she spoke that hinted of the sadness that existed between them. That note in her voice touched his heart. He hated it when she wasn't her normally happy self. But he wasn't happy either, and the only way he would ever be happy was if she said she loved him.

"Okay." He took off his formal coat and white bow tie, then unbuttoned the top button of his tuxedo shirt. "If it takes all night we're going to talk this out." He paused, threw his coat and tie onto a chair, then went to sit on the sofa, never once looking at her as he did so. "I'm going to start out by telling you about the

164

divorce trial but don't interrupt me. I only want to talk about this once."

"I don't think I want to talk about it at all," she protested, perching on the arm of the far side of the sofa.

He reproached her immediately as though he'd expected her argument. "And I told you not to interrupt." He began to speak in a voice lower than normal, almost a monotone. "You know, before I left I told you that Sheila was trying to break a financial trust my father had set up years ago. The trust was not to be touched until my father's death and, thank God, he's still much younger than his years, so the trust has built up for a long time without being disturbed."

Brian looked over at her once, as if to make sure she was listening, then he looked away, staring out toward the gardens, his face a mask. Casey could feel the unspoken bitterness in his words as he told his story.

"I made the mistake once years ago of telling Sheila about it, and she prodded me until I finally told her there was about twenty million dollars in the trust. That was a mistake I later learned to regret."

Even as she listened to him, Casey remembered Brian's telling her that his wife was a compulsively vain woman who tried so hard to look like a scarecrow she could put Twiggy to shame. But it had been very seldom that Brian had mentioned Sheila. Being a gentleman, he followed a rigid code and didn't discuss his problems in any detail.

Casey had always thought his reluctance to talk about his problems had made things worse when she and Brian were on the verge of breaking up. She thought about having met his mother and remembered her aloof manner. Had Brian's mother taught him to keep his problems bottled up inside? Casey thought it was likely.

"When things began to go wrong with us, Sheila let me know right away that she wanted as her share of the divorce settlement a big part of the twenty million dollars. I told her it was impossible and we agreed on a legal separation. That was when I left Pennsylvania and came to Texas. My lawyers were handling everything."

Brian leaned his head against the back of the sofa, closed his eyes, and let out a sigh that was the most intense sound Casey had ever heard. She looked over at him. From three feet away he looked exhausted.

"Sheila had a string of men friends and seemed in no hurry to finalize the divorce after I moved. I thought it was because she was enjoying the monthly maintenance support I was paying her, but I later found out it was because she had hired six lawyers to try to figure out a way to break the trust." He stopped for a second. "I should have known something was wrong when after we'd been separated for eight months she still hadn't agreed to what my lawyers were offering her but by then I had met you, Casey, and I didn't give Sheila another thought. She was just a nuisance from my past." He looked over at Casey and tried to smile, but his mouth only twisted with heavy emotion.

She knew, through his hesitations and the way his voice droned on, that it bothered him to talk about Sheila. It was like reliving the painful past.

"When I told you I was going back to Pennsylvania to settle the divorce case and you insisted upon going

166

along with me, I knew I couldn't let you. By then my attorneys had told me about Sheila and her little scheme to break the trust."

"That's what you said but—" Casey wanted to remind him of how she'd felt at the time, but Brian raised his hand defiantly.

"Casey, let me finish," he complained.

She gave up. He was too intent on having his say to listen to her right now.

"It seems the legal specifics about the trust had been so well written that she couldn't break it. So in her rage Sheila was willing to do whatever she had to do to get money from me. By then she was evidently desperate. When my lawyers called me to return to Pennsylvania they told me some things that she was planning. That was when I decided that no matter what happened I couldn't—I *wouldn't* let you go with me. There was going to be no place for a woman like you in a mud-slinging trial like that one was going to be."

She frowned, wanting to argue with him, but the look on his face warned her not to say a word. She eased down onto the sofa cushion, watching him.

His voice grew stronger, full of conviction. "I was right, Casey, not to let you go with me. Those lawyers of hers sat like a pack of wolves starving for meat. They wanted to name you as corespondent in the case, thinking they could drum up sympathy for Sheila by portraying her as the innocent duped wife and that way get the money Sheila so desperately wanted. They would have ripped a woman like you to shreds. They would have twisted your words and shown you pictures of us together. Their only purpose would have been to discredit you as an honest and innocent woman."

He sighed again and once more the sound wrenched her heart. His words fell down on her like blows. All this time she'd thought he had wanted to handle things in his own solitary way. She'd thought he hadn't loved her enough. Now as she listened to him speak she began to wonder if she'd actually misunderstood him.

"I loved you too much to ever let that happen," Brian added as a postscript to his declaration.

"Pictures?" she questioned him. "You never mentioned pictures before."

"I didn't want to, but I figure the only way I'm going to convince you that I was right to leave you is if I tell you all of it."

"What about pictures?" she asked faintly.

"They'd hired somebody to take pictures of us."

"You and I?" she asked.

He merely nodded.

"Well, I certainly wouldn't have minded having my picture in the courtroom," she exclaimed. "I was proud of being with you."

Brian rolled his eyes skyward and drummed the fingers of his right hand on his kneecap in uncontrolled impatience. "They weren't exactly the kind of pictures you'd want your mother and your aunt to see, Casey."

"Oh." Her voice grew soft. "What kind were they?"

He stood up, unable to stay seated. This was exactly what he'd not wanted to have to tell Casey about. He hadn't wanted to hurt her.

"What kind were they?" she repeated.

Pacing the floor, not looking at her, Brian said,

"They were videotape and thirty-five-millimeter pictures of us in my apartment."

"You mean . . . ?" Casey's throat went dry and she couldn't finish.

"That's exactly what I mean. They had pictures of us in my living room, and they'd managed to make the pictures look worse than they actually were. Evidently they had concealed a hole in the wall and also planted a listening device of some kind. Our conversations were even recorded."

"Oh, Brian, how awful," she whispered, suddenly finding herself unable to sit still. She jumped up to pace beside him. The magnitude of what he'd said began to sink further and further into her thoughts. "How awful," she said again and again.

"How could I have let you go through that? What self-respecting man could drag the woman he loves through something like that? My divorce had nothing to do with you. It was a mistake *I* made and I had to pay for—but not you, Casey."

"I would have withstood it, Brian, if you'd let me," she said, stopping to stand in the middle of the floor. "I loved you."

"If you loved me, then understand, Casey, I couldn't bear to tarnish your name with Sheila's filthy attacks. I know you would have gone with me, but how do you think I could have stood it, day after day, watching them tear you apart in court? As trusting and honest as you are, they would have pounced on anything you'd say and use it to incriminate me, even though legally I was in the right. They would have done everything they could to make our love look sordid." He stopped and stared at her, his voice full of heart wrenching appeal. "I loved you too much to let you suffer those indignities. I was right in what I did."

She stared back at him, taking in the sight of this man who spoke of love and devotion as if those ideals were the most important things in his life. She thought back to how they'd fought, how adamant he'd been that she not go with him.

"Why didn't you explain this before?"

"Because you'd have insisted even more vigorously than before that I take you with me. I was afraid you'd do something crazy like fly up there and appear at the trial even though you knew I didn't want you there."

She swallowed hard. He had to be telling the truth. It made too much sense.

"And, Casey, believe me, it was every bit as nasty as I'd thought it would be. In fact it was worse. I finally bought her off, though, before any of the material surfaced that had anything to do with you."

"You bought her off?"

"It was a small price to pay for my peace of mind. Besides, she sold herself too cheap. Her lawyers ended up with most of the money, and our family ended up with their trust fund intact. I also ended up with all the pictures."

She stood looking at him for a time that had no limitations. With each word it seemed that Brian had made everything but their love diminish in importance, and Casey felt herself overwhelmed with the adjustment her emotions were undergoing.

"Casey, you'll never know how much I wanted your love to be with me this past year. And day by day as the lawyers battled, trying to outwit one another with delays and cancellations, I worried that maybe you'd be gone or married when I came back. When I left and you told me you never wanted to see me again I still knew I'd return. I prayed that when my divorce was final you'd still be free."

He took a step toward her. "It doesn't matter that I love you more than you love me. Nothing matters except that I need to hear you say you love me. Tell me that what I've been through wasn't for nothing."

Casey tried to keep her voice from shaking with the wellspring of her emotions. "You don't love me more than I love you, Brian. You couldn't." Tears sprang to her eyes. "I love you. I've loved you since the moment you first took me into your arms. I'll love you until the last breath." She moved across the room and stood directly in front of him. "Can you ever forgive me?"

She struggled with her tears. "Can you?"

"I'm here, aren't I?" His voice choked with emotion at hearing her say the words he'd waited for, suffered for, longed to hear. "When you love someone you don't look at the past. You live for today."

Great sobs tore through her. "Oh, Brian," she cried. "I love you so."

He took her into his arms, cradling her to him and he could feel her warmth and the jarring movement her body made with each sob. "Don't cry, Casey, not anymore. We have so much to make up for. I want to hear you laugh."

He grazed the top of her head with his lips and basked in her softness. He let his hand swirl in circular patterns around her back, soothing her, calming her. And as he did so he could feel the change within himself.

It was as if now that they had finally come to terms

with the truth they could both relax. They were two people who loved one another, two people who'd faced a problem, stumbled, parted, yet never lost the love they'd shared.

Inside the circle of his arms Casey felt reborn. She felt his warm lips on her face, on her eyelids and throat, and as she reveled in the sensations that were awakening inside her she thought of all the grief she'd suffered without him. "I don't ever want to be without you again, Brian," she murmured as his lips began to move against hers.

Brian moved away from her then and walked to the wall where he turned off the lights. "I don't intend to let you either." He came back for her, took her hand in his, and walked to the front door where he stopped to bolt the lock.

Wrapped in each other's arms, they walked up the staircase and into her bedroom. Brian turned on the light. She reached out a hand to stop him but he wouldn't allow her to touch the control.

"This time, Casey, we give ourselves with no reservations. I love you. You love me."

She gloried in the beauty of his words and the warmth of his gentle touch as he led her to the bed that had felt empty for so long without him.

She wanted to tell him how much she loved him, she wanted to say it again and again, but her words were lost, absorbed in his insistent kiss as he turned her to face him. Her senses were destroyed, the vibrant feel of his rapidly beating heart, the taste of him that seemed always to be so fresh and clean, the rough texture of the skin of his hands as they rubbed first across her arms and then moved to gently knead her back.

"Casey, my Casey," he moaned. He'd never be able to get enough of her. Enveloping her into his arms, he pulled her nearer, wanting nothing more or less than to be with her forever.

Feeling fully alive, like a prisoner set free, Casey smiled up at him as Brian moved his hands to the top of the heavy zipper of her jumpsuit. As her physical need combined with her love of him, she felt time slip away and bury itself. She put every thought behind her save her love for him.

Through the shadow of her lashes Casey swept her eyes along the lower curve of his face, taking in the gentle slope of his lips. She moved her gaze up to his eyes and watched the way they moved lovingly from her face to the top of her jumpsuit.

His overwhelming sensuality was communicated to her without benefit of words or gestures. With Brian it seemed that she took on, through his influence, that same power. She felt bewitched and bewitching, as if she were the most sexual of beings. There was no shame, only glory.

Brian slowly moved his hand downward, peeling the zipper with him. There was a sound of metal scraping metal within the quiet room and then it stopped. He could not resist running his hand across the planes of her throat and below. Her skin felt smooth and hot to the touch as though all the heat inside her body had surfaced and come to rest on the outer layer of her skin.

Everywhere his fingers touched she seemed hot, and he gazed into her face, noticing the brightness of her cheeks. His mouth closed over hers, moving back and forth with passionate insistence.

She shivered with the lust he evoked. With trembling hands she reached up to grasp his head. Her fingers couldn't be still and she found herself touching his hair, swirling her fingers in and out of the dark mass until she discovered a tender spot of flesh on his neck. There was a special feeling she noticed at the line where his hair stopped and his nape began. Gently she started to knead the tender flesh there, and she knew there would always be a very specialness about Brian, no matter where it was that she touched him. To her everything about Brian was unique.

He took a long-awaited delight in feeling her hand move through his hair and along his neckline. The warmth of her body fused him with euphoric abandon. He bent his head closer, lost in the fever of his passion.

Profoundly aware of all the sensations she was experiencing, Casey could feel Brian's heart pounding against his chest as he buried her head into his neck, hugging her to him with an increasingly tight embrace. And then he moved ever so slightly and his mouth was once more caressing her lips with the gentlest of brushstrokes.

He wanted to go slow, take his time, hoping to give her the ultimate, the maximum pleasure he could, but every part of his body was alive with desire and his hold on his passion was fragile, ready to snap at any time.

Casey's senses swam with desire as the intensity of her feelings made her arch her body to his, her breasts tingling with exquisite sensitivity—hard and responsive. Brian kissed her again, long and wanting and fierce this time.

Her tongue tasted sweet. It flayed inside his mouth until he wanted to explode.

His mouth left her lips and she gasped as he kissed her throat, one hand brushing her side as it swept around to once more reach the zipper of her jumpsuit. He eased it downward until his hands could freely explore, then begin to trace an outline of each breast.

She moaned softly and he began to massage each soft round breast in very slow concentric circles. Every now and then he would bring his lips down to first lick each hard nipple then ever so gently allow his front teeth to graze against them, sending her body into spasms as she responded to the overloading of her senses.

He lost himself in the fragrant softness of her cleavage, burying his face as he pushed aside her new satin bra, unfastening its front hook so quickly that she didn't know that he had even done so. In one flashing move Brian jammed the zipper of her jumpsuit down, took both breasts within his grasp and pushed them toward his face as Casey gently stepped out of her crumpled clothing. With idly circling thumbs he coaxed each breast to grow more heated and rigid.

When he brought his head up, her breasts suddenly felt cool then cold, as if they were meant to be warmed only from his nurturing caress. She watched in amazement as he shed his clothes and slipped down the covers of her bed, taking less time than seemed possible.

Brian turned back to look at her, and in the glow of the overhead light there were no concealing shadows. Contrary to her expectations she felt no embarrassment as she was standing before him. She caught his stare as he looked at her and she found herself smiling. She could tell that he was pleased with what he saw, and she brought her hands up to her hips, playfully displaying her nakedness. But Brian's look was too intense to be humorous and she stepped into his open arms.

When in his presence she felt that she was a sexual being who would give pleasure to the man she loved in any way she could. She basked in the pleasure she had seen in his pale-gray eyes and she felt a distinctive pride in being comfortable with her own body.

He stopped to look at her once again, and she felt a magnificent shiver run from the base of her spine out to all the parts of her body. Wherever he touched her with his eyes, her body responded. Unable to keep her emotions in check, she eased her way onto the bed and looked up at him, begging him without words to join her.

When he stretched his long frame beside her on the bed and took her into his arms, she felt a peacefulness settle around her heart and she knew she had at last found her perfect man. There was something that she wanted to say but her lips would not form the words. Instead her mind was directing all its attention to the surge of desire within her, the overwhelming flood of sensations she was experiencing.

Brian bent over her, his lips grazing her chin, her throat, and then down an imaginary straight line, stopping to pause at the center of her waist. Her love made him want to taste every part of her, every delicate spot, and he made his way to her thighs where he let his tongue caress her in exquisite exploration.

He spread her beautiful legs and continued his kisses until he felt her begin to moan and writhe under the spell of his kiss. Then he gently caressed her, finding what he'd been searching for, and causing her to gasp aloud in pleasure.

"Oh, Brian, please," she begged.

When he entered her, it seemed her pleasure was too immense, driving her insane, and she reached out for him, lashing against his bare back with nails that could not be sheathed. She was caught up in ecstasy and there was no reasoning here, no rational thinking, only the most powerful feeling on earth.

As Brian felt her quivering below him, he began to thrust into her, harder and faster until his thrusts became uncontrollable and the two of them were caught up in an onrushing orgasm that came like a hard bolt of lightning, striking them both to the core.

Hours later when they were both well past the point of exhaustion, Brian lifted her up and settled her down on top of him. "Look at me, Casey," he murmured through passion-ravaged lips. When he was sure she was meeting his eyes with her own, he said, "When I wake up, Casey. I want to find you next to me so I know this wasn't all a dream."

She nodded her head. She took one of his hands and began to kiss each fingertip softly, her eyes half closed, relishing the taste of his skin.

"I want you with me tonight," he said, and pulled her down beside him, then covered them both with the sheet. "Stay with me, Casey," he whispered as he closed his eyes. "Stay with me."

CHAPTER TEN

"This is just what I wanted," he whispered into her ear sometime late the next morning.

"Mmm, me too," she answered, giggling at the way her inner ear tickled when he spoke into it.

Brian snuggled up to her, his body planed to her back, his hand cupped around her bare breast. Muted sunlight broke through the curtains and fell in diamondlike patterns across their faces.

"Tell me you love me," he demanded, nipping at her ear with his lips. "Tell me."

"I love you." Casey turned toward him, throwing her arms up around his neck, letting her fingers fall down to caress the crisp texture of his hair.

"Say it again."

"I love you," she answered with a laugh and a kiss on his nose.

"Every morning of our lives I want to wake up to that laugh." Brian planted two soft kisses on either side of her mouth. "But this morning I have some things to do, so I'm going to have to leave you now."

"What?" She moaned. "Are you kidding?"

"Nope." He threw off the covers, then bent down to kiss her once again. "I'm not kidding."

"Brian, are you going to work?" she asked gloomily. Casey had harbored delicious visions of the two of them spending the morning, perhaps the entire day, in bed.

"Nope."

"Are you going to tell me where you're going?" she demanded.

Brian shrugged his way into the clothes he'd so hastily discarded the night before. "It's a secret."

"For me?"

"It can't be for me." He laughed, trying to button the buttons on his tuxedo shirt. "You be ready at six o'clock this evening. Wear something pretty, something a little fancy, something special."

"You mean it's going to take you all day, this secret of yours?"

He walked over to the edge of the bed and looked down at her, still smiling. "It's almost eleven o'clock. Did you know that?" He showed her his watch, then impatiently yanked off the shirt he couldn't manage to button.

"I was thinking that maybe I'd fix you a little breakfast and then you could go on your merry way." She wanted to postpone his leaving any way she could. Now that they were together, she didn't want to let him go. "I could eat a horse, couldn't you?"

"To be honest with you, Casey, if I stayed, I'd rather climb back into that soft bed of yours. My hunger is not exactly for a horse right now, but you go ahead and cook yourself one if you want." He started out of the room.

"No, then I'd get fat again," she complained.

"More to love." He stuck his head back inside the

179

doorway. "Eat the horse if you want it. Just be ready at six o'clock."

"I love you, Brian," she called after him, feeling like the luckiest woman in the world.

"And I love you," he called before she heard the door slam behind him.

At six o'clock she stood looking out the front door. Dressed and ready since five-thirty, Casey could hardly wait to see him again. Overnight her life had changed, and it was such a wonderful experience she wanted to pinch herself to make certain it had all really happened.

It was just as she'd known it would be with Brian. Being in love changed everything around her. It was as if a touch of magic had been sprinkled all over her existence and it was a wonderful thing.

"Here I am," Brian called as he pulled his Mercedes up to the curb and got out.

She started out to meet him, walking at first and then breaking into a run. In her high heels she knew she could twist her ankle, but seeing him and being in his arms was more important than any ankle might be.

"Hello, my love," he said, lifting her up in his arms.

"I thought you'd never get here," she answered happily.

"You look beautiful."

Casey wore a satin skirt and blouse of peacock blue and a strand of freshwater pearls around her neck. Her cheeks glowed with love and her eyes were clear, their blue-green color bright and sparkling.

"You . . . you look like you haven't changed clothes." She giggled.

Brian was dressed in his tuxedo, handsomely

groomed. He acknowledged her giggle with a smile of his own.

"You're almost right. I had to have these clothes cleaned this afternoon. It seems you wrinkled them last night when you were trying to entice me up to your bedroom."

"Ho, ho, ho," she teased. "I thought it was a mutual enticement."

"It was," he whispered before kissing her. "Come on."

He whisked her into the car, refusing to answer any of her questions about where they were going or what plans he'd made for them. He drove to Lake Austin and stopped in front of an exclusive restaurant he'd taken Casey to one time last year.

"Is it open?" she asked, noticing there were no other cars in the main parking lot.

"Oh, yes," he answered knowingly and led her inside.

The restaurant foyer was dimly lit. A hostess greeted them with what Casey thought was a funny smile. She guided them down terrazzo steps into the two-storied main dining area. Throughout the room round tables were set with immaculately starched and pressed linen cloths. The chairs were French, upholstered in pink silk, and each table gleamed with delicate crystal and shining silver pieces. Flowers and lighted candles were everywhere, even on the white marble fireplace that was used in the winter. Toward the lake the walls were composed of square panes of glass and Casey could see the water out through the distance.

Brian walked with his hand on Casey's back and she

could feel his eyes on her as she looked all around the room. It was magnificent but strangely silent.

The hostess led them across the wooden dance square in the center of the room and then to a table that had an even more bountiful centerpiece of flowers —day lilies, tea roses, garden fern, and daisies. Once Casey was seated Brian sat down across from her.

"Are we the only ones here?" she asked in a whisper.

"Yes." Brian motioned toward a double door.

A waiter hurried toward them, then two, then three. Suddenly the room was filling up with people. With instruments in hand, Casey saw men begin to fill up the orchestra section behind the dance floor.

"Brian, what is it? What's going on?"

"It's our first official night together and I didn't want any intrusions," he said, before instructing the waiter to bring them the champagne he'd ordered earlier.

"Well, it doesn't look very crowded."

"That's because we're going to be the only ones here." He waited until the orchestra began to play a slow love song. "May I have this dance?"

"You mean you arranged all of this?"

"Right down to the meal. I hope you like roast duck."

"Oh, Brian, this is wonderful," Casey cried as he led her out to the dancefloor and from somewhere in the distance someone dimmed the lights.

"Being with you is wonderful." He held her tightly and twirled her around the room, watching how her eyes sparkled.

After a few moments he put his chin against the top

of her head, nestling her face against his shoulder. He felt like he'd finally found his contentment, and he told himself not to ever let go of the feeling.

The orchestra didn't stop playing until Brian motioned them to do so. He led Casey back to her seat.

"I ordered champagne." Brian picked up two silver goblets from the table and stood beside her. "A toast to you, my love," he said.

Strains of soft music filled the room and she could smell the delicate odor of the fresh flowers. Raising her goblet to her lips, Casey imagined this might be the most romantic evening of her life.

"I love you," she murmured before sipping the sweet champagne.

"Drink up, Casey. I ordered a magnum."

They drank again. She felt something tap her tooth and although she knew it couldn't be, she thought something was in her drink. Not wanting to make a spectacle of herself, Casey blinked, then looked down inside her goblet.

"What is this?" she cried, putting two fingers into the cool champagne.

"My, my," he said, watching her. "Will wonders never cease?"

Tears stung her eyes when she retrieved the object, but these were tears of joy. "Oh, Brian, it's beautiful."

"If you don't like it, I'll be happy to take you back with me tomorrow and you can pick out your own. I didn't know they cut diamonds in so many shapes."

"Oh, no, it's perfect." Casey held up a platinum ring with a large heart-shaped diamond gleaming in its center.

"Will you marry me, Casey? I meant what I said

183

last night. I don't want to ever be without you again."
Brian spoke in a voice that was quivering with overwhelming emotion.

"I've never wanted anything so much in my life,"
Casey answered, wiping away a tear.

"We'll get the license tomorrow."

He slipped the ring on her finger. Then he kissed
her hand.

"It's the most beautiful ring I ever saw," she told
him.

"And you're the most beautiful woman I ever saw,"
he said, taking her into his arms.

The orchestra began to play another love song, and
as they danced Casey knew she was living the most
romantic night of her life. Caught up in the magic of
the evening, they danced their way around the room, a
lone couple, full of love and joy.

Much later that night they returned to Casey's
house.

"Where will we live, Casey?" Brian held her hand
as they walked toward the back door.

"Brian, I honestly don't care. I like both our houses.
Yours is so much larger, but . . . oh, Brian, I'm so
happy I don't care about the house or anything else. I
just want to be with you."

They reached the door and he took her key from her
to unlock it. "Okay, we'll worry about that later, although I like my swimming pool."

The thought of the swimming pool made her giggle.
"There's something I have to tell you, Brian, something you need to know before we get married."

"What's that?" he said, opening the door and reaching inside to turn on the kitchen light.

"I can't swim."

He looked at her with widened eyes. "You're kidding."

"No, I'm the original athletic dud. I don't know how I got across the pool the other night at your house. Maybe it was fear that kept me on top of the water."

He began to laugh then, taking in great gulps of air. "I don't believe you."

"While we're at it," she charged on, "I might as well confess everything. When you left Austin I decided that you were the antithesis of what I wanted in a man. You were too rich, too attractive, too athletic, and too strong-willed. That's what I told myself anyway."

He was still laughing but he put his hands on her waist after he closed the door behind them. "And now what have you decided?"

"Well, until you reminded me of your trust fund I'd convinced myself that just starting out with a new paper meant you were in debt, and when you scratched your cheek I decided that too handsome could be ruled out and . . ." She took a deep breath. "And then with your running your bike into a rock I decided that maybe you weren't the athlete I'd imagined you to be, and . . ." She took another breath. "And you're still too strong-willed but every now and then you have a real knack for tenderheartedness."

He swung her around the room, his laughter never stopping. "Oh, Casey, you're the only woman I'll ever want. You're also the funniest."

She broke out into that quick bolt of laughter of hers, ending with a gurgle just as Brian's lips swept down to claim her, and pleasure of his company mixed with the desire his touch always sparked within her. She knew they were going to have a most delightful life together.

Later when they were undressed, Casey said, "Brian, would you mind if I went downstairs for a minute? There's something I've got to do."

"As long as you go with no clothes on, so I'll be sure that you can't escape me," he teased.

She left him with a kiss and a promise to return, then hurried down the stairs to her study. She turned on the brass table light and smiled happily to herself like a little girl who'd discovered the magic of Christmas.

There were some truths throughout the world, and Casey knew one of them to be that love was the most important emotion a person could have. Having Brian's love made her feel as if there were nothing she couldn't do, nothing she couldn't have. She felt as if the peace they shared would enable her to always be whatever she wanted to be.

She reached into the drawer and pulled out the beautiful book and pen her mother had given her. *There is nothing I can't do now,* she thought.

In quick, bold strokes she began to write:

Heart of a Gypsy
by Casey Clayton Powell

On this particular day in Houston, Texas, the sky was the color of faded denim, bleached out by

the piercing sun which blared down from overhead. Sunny McQueen sat on the hot cement
curb, straining her ears for the jingling sound of
the Good Humor ice cream truck.

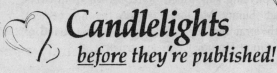

ON LEAVING CHARLESTON
ALEXANDRA RIPLEY

Live this
magnificent
family saga
—from the
civilized,
ante-bellum South
through the wreckless,
razzle-dazzle Jazz Age

Southern heiress Garden Tradd sheds the traditions
of her native Charleston to marry the rich, restless
Yankee, Sky Harris. Deeply in love, the happy young
couple crisscross the globe to hobnob with society in
Paris, London, and New York. They live a fast-paced,
fairy-tale existence, until the lovely Garden discovers
that her innocence and wealth are no insulation against
the magnitude of unexpected betrayal. In desperation
the gentle woman seeks refuge in the city she had once
abandoned, her own, her native land—Charleston.

$3.95   16610-1-17

As advertised on TV

Catch SPRING FEVER with Dell

At your local bookstore or use this handy coupon for ordering:

Dell

DELL READERS SERVICE—DEPT. BR780B
P.O. BOX 1000. PINE BROOK. N.J. 07058

Please send me the above title(s). I am enclosing $ _____ (please add 75c per copy to cover
postage and handling). Send check or money order—no cash or COOs. Please allow 3-4 weeks for shipment.
CANADIAN ORDERS: please submit in U.S. dollars.

Ms Mrs Mr _____

Address_____

City State_____ Zip _____

Rebels and outcasts, they fled halfway across the earth to settle the harsh Australian wastelands. Decades later—ennobled by love and strengthened by tragedy—they had transformed a wilderness into fertile land. And themselves into

WILLIAM STUART LONG

THE EXILES, #1	12374-7-12	$3.95
THE SETTLERS, #2	17929-7-45	$3.95
THE TRAITORS, #3	18131-3-21	$3.95
THE EXPLORERS, #4	12391-7-11	$3.50
THE ADVENTURERS, #5	10330-4-40	$3.95
THE COLONISTS, =6	11342-3-21	$3.95

All-new
Candlelight
Newsletter

**An exceptional,
free offer awaits readers
of Dell's incomparable Candlelight Ecstasy and Supreme Romances.**

Subscribe to our all-new CANDLELIGHT NEWSLETTER
and you will receive—at absolutely no cost to you—exciting, exclusive information about today's finest romance novels and nov-
elists. You'll be part of a select group to receive sneak previews of
upcoming Candlelight Romances, well in advance of publication.

You'll also go behind the scenes to "meet" our Ecstasy and
Supreme authors, learning firsthand where they get their
ideas and how they made it to the top. News of author appear-
ances and events will be detailed, as well. And contributions from
the Candlelight editor will give you the inside scoop on how she
makes her decisions about what to publish—and how *you* can try
your hand at writing an Ecstasy or Supreme.

You'll find all this and more in Dell's CANDLELIGHT
NEWSLETTER. And best of all, *it costs you nothing*. That's right!
It's Dell's way of thanking our loyal Candlelight readers and of
adding another dimension to your reading enjoyment.

Just fill out the coupon below, return it to us, and look forward to receiving the first of many CANDLELIGHT NEWS-
LETTERS—overflowing with the kind of excitement that only
enhances our romances!

| **Dell** | **DELL READERS SERVICE—DEPT. BR780E** |
| | **P.O. BOX 1000. PINE BROOK. N.J. 07058** |

Name_____

Address_____

City_____

State_____ Zip_____